# INSIDE THE F.B.I.

By NORMAN OLLESTAD

# *Inside The F.B.I.*

*1967*

LYLE STUART • NEW YORK

My deep appreciation to Bill Cleary for his invaluable contribution to the writing of this book.

# INSIDE THE F.B.I.

"The call of the future must be a re-kindled American faith, based on our priceless heritage of freedom, justice, and the religious spirit."

J. Edgar Hoover, *Masters of Deceit*

# 1

It began as a routine day, a pretty dull one at that. The sun climbed high into a postcard Miami sky. It was toward the end of the season, in April, and hot as only Miami can be. Not a breath of wind stirred the brackish sea-surface under the causeway.

We'd been interviewing some criminal informants over in Hollywood when the call came on the car radio from the Miami Beach police. The security officers over at the Hotel Fontainebleau were holding a bad-check writer, and they had also recognized him from one of our circulars as an armed robbery suspect.

I thought sure the *Cracker* would turn on the siren when we got the call, but he didn't. He just swung the old grey F.B.I. sedan onto the 79th Street causeway, cut over into the left lane and held the speedometer at a steady sixty. That was where he wanted to be. I didn't say anything about the siren. For one thing I had been with the Miami field office only a little over a month, and I considered myself damned lucky that Special Agent I. A. Spence, better known as the

"Georgia Cracker," put up with me at all. He had made it well known that he didn't relish "young punk agents" tagging along and getting in the way.

I glanced at the Cracker. The sweat clung to his forehead beneath a tangle of straight black hair. It wasn't long, just too straight and determined in its own direction to stay where it was supposed to. His shirt collar had rolled up like soggy potato chips in the wet Miami heat. I was in my shirt sleeves, but he still wore his coat. He always wore it. I seldom wore mine unless the situation was tense enough for firearms, and then it was necessary to wear it to cover up the gun.

"Now these armed robbers, they're an ugly breed, boy. . . ." The Cracker startled me. His eyes stared straight ahead, the words tumbling slowly in his thick Georgia drawl. And he always called me "boy." That really got on my nerves at first. "They're crazy for fightin'," he added. "And I don't want you thinkin' you can always go out and bring in guys like this one single handed. . . ." I waited for him to continue but he was preoccupied with wiping the sweat from his eyebrows.

Up ahead the beach traffic was thickening as we neared Miami Beach. A slow moving sportscar with New York plates and a golden girl in a bright pink cocktail outfit at the wheel edged into our lane.

The Cracker checked the mirror, then swung around her on the right. She gave us a startled look as we flew by. She hadn't the faintest idea we were the F.B.I. The wind rumpled her hair as she tossed her head and I smiled, thinking how much she reminded me of the girl I'd spent my last summer surfing with in Malibu. But that all vanished as the end of the causeway appeared up ahead, and the Cracker turned to me without taking his eyes from the traffic and grunted, "Got your gun, boy?"

I froze. My hand snapped automatically to my hip. The pistol. It wasn't there! I was speechless. Not wanting to wear the coat I'd left my .38 back at the office. The Cracker glanced down and saw my hand frozen where the holster should have been at my belt, and from my expression he knew what had happened. But he said nothing. It would have been a waste of time. There would simply be one less man to help. Such was the Cracker's style.

We turned off the causeway, then right on Collins Avenue, and a moment later the alabaster walls of the Fontainebleau swept into view before us. The Cracker pulled up in front of the marble staircase leading up to the security office on the second floor. He left the engine running. Snatching his hat from the back seat, he started out the door, then hesitated as he turned to me. "Now what you do, boy, is drive the car over to that entrance . . ." He gestured toward the canopied walkway to the downstairs lobby. "See it?" I nodded. "You just wait there . . . and keep that engine running!"

He slammed the door and started up the stairs. I slid across the seat and maneuvered the old sedan over in front of the lobby and parked there, watching the tourists walk in and out for the next twenty minutes. I never even heard the shooting till it was all over and a man lay dead.

But even as we were pulling up in front of the Fontainebleau, our suspect had broken away from the guards, shooting one of them through the neck. The remaining two were locked in their office and the criminal fled downstairs— straight into the path of the Georgia Cracker. He saw the bulge beneath the agent's coat and went wild, scrambling back through the second floor lobby, drawing his pistol as he ran. He got off three wild shots at the Cracker, who was now in hot pursuit.

Guests, room clerks and bellboys alike—all stood in their tracks, not truly comprehending what was happening before them . . . as the Cracker went coolly about his business. He held his fire. The distance was too great and the veritable forest of marble columns in the Fontainebleau foyer would have caused stray bullets to ricochet. The agent jogged straight through the lobby, paused for an instant at the door used only moments before by the killer.

A shot rang out. A woman screamed. Chunks of plaster flew about the room like shotgun pellets, and the Cracker glanced up at the hole the size of a man's fist in the brocade over the doorway, only a few feet from his head. He pressed on.

Peering around the corner and out into the parking lot, the Cracker glimpsed his man ducking behind a shiny Cadillac limousine. Running crouched and crablike, he traversed the open area between the hotel and the parking lot; the pistol barked twice from behind the limousine and the Cracker dove headlong into the gravel beneath the first row of cars. He rolled to his feet, then cocked his head to one side, listening. No sound came from the direction of the Cadillac. He hesitated a moment longer, then darted behind the next car. The gravel crunched softly with each step. Still nothing.

He cut across three rows, then slid behind a Greyhound bus whose driver sat inside eating his lunch and reading the paper while his portable radio blared, completely unaware of what was going on outside. Peering cautiously around the back of the bus, the Cracker saw a dark figure huddled by the rear door of the limousine, only thirty yards away, his hands jerking feverishly as they crammed bullets into the revolver's cylinder.

The agent watched for a long moment. The criminal lurched to his feet, snapped the cylinder shut and looked about wildly, never noticing the stooped and darkened form of the agent at the rear of the bus as he brought his revolver up slowly with his right hand, then steadied it with his left. There were only the soft clicking sounds as the Cracker slid his thumb back over the hammer to cock it and the sharp explosion as the gun jumped once and the man collapsed, shot through the head, dead.

The Cracker was silent all the way back to the F.B.I. garage. After we had checked out for the day and we were ready to leave, he turned to me with an expression on his weather-beaten face I was to see only one other time during my career with the Miami Bureau. "Believe me, boy, I hated to do it . . ." His voice was hoarse and low, almost a whisper. "But he should of known better than to tangle with the F.B.I."

And today when somebody asks me about my career with the Federal Bureau of Investigation I always think first of the Georgia Cracker.

# 2

But this was just one incident in the F.B.I., and the Cracker was but a single man. There was also Murph the Surf, my Miami surfing buddy who later robbed the American Museum of Natural History and made off with a priceless collection of rare gems, among them the Star of India sapphire. And there was the beautiful young girl named Judy whom I'll never forget, but whose father turned out to be a notorious gangster; and, too, there was the ill-fated Bay of Pigs invasion . . . but these were a far cry from the beginning. Malibu came first.

In Malibu the sun had been my star, guiding me through the undergraduate years at U.C.L.A., and then through law school. For those seven years I lived on the Malibu beach called Topanga where the canyon, also Topanga, and its tiny river emptied into the sea, then rose upward and widened into the valley, which grew and grew, finally melding into the Los Angeles basin where six million people lived beneath the blanket of smog. Here, at Topanga, at the mouth of the city were the sun and the sea—and the surf, which fused the better parts of two alien worlds.

They were good years. And between classes at the university and my part-time job in the chemistry library I rode waves endlessly; I lay in the sand, a sun-blackened seal. But it could only last so long. Surfing is like that. Either it wins or you do; there is no compromise. And for those seven years the surf pounded, argued incessantly against a steady job and civic responsibility, against the ideals of those six million in the basin. How easily I might have followed the surf.

Like all students, I suppose, toward the end of my undergraduate years I began to change. Among many things, I learned that it was often they who demanded their rights most fiercely who used them to abuse the freedoms of others.

And, too, during my senior year I had visited India on a U.S. State Department sponsored goodwill tour where I learned another important lesson: that the things men speak of are often a far cry from the things they do. There, in India, I met for the first time young people my own age who passionately embraced the doctrines of communism. Grand were their eulogies of the "Soviet experiment"; but grand also were their other ambitions. How, they would ask me, might they be able to come to *America?* Of course, I had no idea. But did they not want to visit the Soviet Union? No, they did not. That was that.

It was only natural, I guess, that I had come to realize something in life beyond the waves.

After graduation, law school was not an illogical choice. The profession was respectable, and it seemed like the best way to serve the principles of my country. Three years later, on a hot September afternoon, I coaxed my '47 vintage Chevrolet away from the university and through the rush-hour traffic that jammed the streets of the university city, thoroughly exhausted by the California bar examination which I had just completed. If I passed, a good offer from a large Beverly Hills law firm awaited. But that was at least several months off; the results would not be known until sometime in November. And right now the sun blazed and the best surf of the season was rolling in at Topanga and I was prepared to enjoy it . . . if only I could get out of the city!

Up ahead the signal changed. Nothing happened. My lane didn't budge. Right in front of me stood the reason. A greying woman in her forties sat behind the wheel of her lavender Cadillac and calmly freshened her makeup; a miniature Schnauzer charged around in the back seat, barking. I glanced into the mirror and swung around her into the other lane. The Schnauzer barked from the window, directly at me it seemed. She was oblivious. I reached the signal just as it turned red again, and my old Chevy barely made the stop.

The light turned green and I gunned the engine only to slam on the brakes again before I had gone more than a few feet. I watched as a bespangled dowager in tight capri pants stepped down off the curb, her arms loaded with packages, and strolled casually across against the light, rolling her hips in a grotesque travesty. My god! I thought. Her poor husband. And I was suddenly transfixed by the dawning realization that these women were from the same indelible mold as the wives of my future law associates, a number of whom I had met at a recent cocktail party. Would I marry one of them, too?

All the way home I daydreamed of my law career, and I tried to shrug off the nightmarish hallucinations of those Cadillac-clad dowagers in capri pants, but for the first time since I'd made up my mind to study law the plan didn't set so well. As I swung around the last curve in the coast highway, the gentle cove of Topanga swept into view; a glassy ground swell rose and fell at the point, driving all thoughts of the future from me.

A golden sun was just sinking into the sea as I paddled my

surfboard out through the waves. The wind had stopped; the stillness was overwhelming.

As I neared my favorite take-off spot at the point where the waves were biggest and fastest and where the challenge was best I stopped paddling and coasted, resting on my knees, waiting. A glassy swell rushed in toward the point, hesitated, then broke with a sharp crack. I sat off to the side and watched it, gauging its course. Perfect. In a moment the next one came sliding over the outside reef, rising higher than its brother. And as it came I dug once with my arms, and at once I was sliding with the wave, feeling the rush of the wind and the shiny skin of the wave peeling beneath me. My board and I ran trim and together with the wave, much as the sailor or the skier does in his own element. Only this one was mine. Always, everything here was the same. The waves built before me, urging me to forget.

But today, for some reason the surfing was not so good as it usually was, and after only a few rides I paddled in. Something deep within me said, "You've got two months to think things out. Use them."

And I did. Before the first month had passed I was pretty sure that the grand promise of a junior partnership with the law firm after ten years of legal research . . . and the grim nightmare of a marriage to one of their women were not for me. But what was? I didn't know. I surfed and lay in the sand and talked to my friends, but their eyes followed only the waves. They had no answers. The only thing I did know for sure was that life meant more than a monotonous and unproductive progression of part-time jobs and surf-safaris from California to Hawaii.

Then one morning at breakfast I read in the paper a fascinating account of how the F.B.I. had cracked another "perfect murder." Miraculously, they had traced a microscopic sample of silk fibre found in a New York apartment, the scene of the crime, to a Japanese silk plantation and hence to a Hong Kong shop where the murderer's custom suit was made for him. Only a few days later he was apprehended in Los Angeles where he had fled in the wake of his crime. He was so surprised when the agents placed him under arrest that he confessed at once. And in a final, poetic outburst the journalist penned his closing line: ". . . just another in that incredible procession of victories over the powers of evil by those men in blue, the agents of the F.B.I." Somewhere in the back of my mind I could hear the band playing . . . could almost see those legions of F.B.I. men striding across the newsreel screen.

But there over my breakfast, it was that one line that took me back to a bleak Monday morning several months before when a pair of agents had addressed our class at law school. They spoke of their "Washington Bureau without civil service, without a single political appointee. A bureau without bureaucrats!"

I remember their words and the staccato cadence of their speech as they spelled out Bureau requirements: *"American citizenship . . . between the ages of twenty-three and forty . . . of balanced moral character . . . excellent scholastic and employment records . . . credit rating, calibre of associates, reputation and general fitness must be found excellent!"* I remember remarking to myself on the toughness of those requirements. But it was their physical conditioning program that fascinated me. A program that was considered so sound by the armed forces that even our own American commandos of World War II were trained by none other than the F.B.I. instructors.

At the time, though, the idea of a Bureau career never

even entered my mind. But over these last few months things had changed. I had changed. A career among those lean hard men who served and protected the principles of American democracy . . . why hadn't I thought of the Bureau before?

It was like a dream. I remember driving into town and parking my battered Chevy two blocks away from the Los Angeles field office, because I was afraid someone might see it. And the next thing I knew I was shaking hands with Special Agent James Fitzpatrick, who made me comfortable in a chair across from his desk. And after we had exchanged a few remarks about the weather, and after he commented on my suntan, he got down to the business of interviewing me for a job as a special agent of the Federal Bureau of Investigation.

He began with the manner of polite authority for which the Bureau has become universally famous. "I see from your application that you were ranked 84th in your class of 145 at U.C.L.A. Law School. Is that correct?" He looked up from the application and leaned back in his chair, appraising me with his cool grey eyes.

"Yes, sir," I replied, "that is correct." I looked directly at him; it seemed like the thing to do.

"Well, let's see," said the agent. He glanced back at the application. "I believe your time was divided while you were in school," he added diplomatically.

"Yes, it was. I had a part-time job in the chemistry library . . ." I was about to add that I'd also spent quite a bit of time surfing, but I thought better of it as he continued.

"Ah, yes, it's all down here on the form." He looked pleased that I'd filled it out quite perfectly. "Now, Mr. Ollestad, before we continue are there any questions you would like to ask me about the F.B.I.?"

Fitzpatrick was a clever man. Perceptive. A trained interviewer. I would be frank with him. "Yes," I began somewhat uncertainly. "I saw on the Agent's Qualification Sheet that the F.B.I. requires twenty-twenty vision and no physical defects that might impair an agent's ability to handle firearms . . ."

The agent appraised me coolly. "That's pretty self-explanatory," he said. "What's the problem?"

"Well . . . I need glasses," I confessed. "And the army has classified me 4-F. . . ."

"For defective vision?" His brow furrowed.

"No, a physical defect. I've got a damaged cartilage in my left knee." That did it, I thought. And they probably would never have discovered it at all.

Fitzpatrick smiled. He looked relieved. "No problem, Ollestad. A large percentage of our agents wear glasses to correct their vision to twenty-twenty. Don't worry about that. If you can pass the physical examination *our* doctors will give you, you'll be accepted regardless of any loose or unnecessary cartilage." I relaxed. But his smile faded and he leaned forward over his desk and his cool grey eyes turned to steel as he added, "But one thing is vitally important, Ollestad—something that we will not compromise on. And that's your background. Your philosophy of life. Your attitudes . . . and what goes on inside your head."

The agent frowned, then pulled back in his chair and stood up, all the while watching me. He paced back and forth slowly as he spoke. "I want to know if you've ever been in any kind of trouble with the law. Like drinking beer on the beach. Or financial trouble. Like not paying your fraternity bill on time. Or girl trouble. Like not being aggressive enough with the sorority girls . . . and having the word get around all over campus. Know what I mean,

Ollestad? *Trouble*." He dropped his eyes back to the form for an instant, then shot them up into mine. "Ollestad, I must know if you are *clean!*"

But this was just the beginning. For the next three hours Fitzpatrick grilled me, determined to find out if I were politically, financially, philosophically and morally sterile.

"Did you ever take part in any kind of political activity while you were in school?"

"No."

He frowned. "Ever been in any financial trouble . . . ever fail to pay back any student loans?"

"No . . ." I glanced up to find him glaring at me. "No . . . *sir*," I added. The agent must have liked that better because he looked back at his notes and continued his probing into matters whose significance I would only learn in the months to follow. More than once during Fitzpatrick's full-scale interrogation I was asked if there were "any skeletons" in my closet. There were not. All answers were negative. And after a month and a half of checking my background, after interviewing my law school and college associates, the Bureau finally permitted me to take the written and physical examinations. I passed.

# 3

It was an icy morning in late November when I arrived in our nation's capital, leaving the sun and the Malibu surf and the beach called Topanga forever behind me. But with my letter from J. Edgar Hoover tucked securely inside my breast pocket, I stood confident on the threshold of a new world as Washington prepared for the holiday season.

Overhead, Christmas bloomed with tinsel and scattered effigies of Santa. It was early. I had taken the night flight from Los Angeles, but those tiny sandwiches and that synthetic orange juice they served on the plane were hardly sufficient for a special agent of the F.B.I.

I dragged my heavy suitcase past frosted store windows filled with toys and through the nearly empty sidewalks for half an hour before I found a restaurant that was open. Noting a sign that advertised "huevos rancheros" over the door as I entered, I found an empty table. Half a dozen bleary-eyed customers mulled over the coffee and the morning newspaper at the counter. I gave my order for the Spanish ranch-style eggs, and when the waitress served me she looked me straight in the eye and asked matter-of-factly, "How's the weather in California this time of year?"

"Great," I answered. "But how'd you . . . ?"

"Easy," she laughed, revealing a terrible set of teeth. The waitress busied herself, cleaning up the table next to mine, then turned and jerked an ungraceful thumb toward my plate. "Not very many people order *that* for breakfast you know. Besides you don't have a hat. Nobody from California wears a hat. You work here long enough and you get used to that sort of thing." With that she vanished into the kitchen.

Me . . . in a hat? I thought. Never. Back at home they'd have laughed me off the beach. Only old men wear hats, and nobody wants to be an old man so nobody wears one. But in a few months I'd be Special Agent Norman Ollestad of the F.B.I. One day soon I'd break a big case, handcuff some dangerous criminal and throw him in jail. And I'd have to have a hat. All F.B.I. men wear hats. Everybody knows that.

I gobbled down my breakfast, paid the check to another giggling waitress and retreated with my suitcase out the door and across the street to a department store where a large, giggling salesgirl pointed the way to men's haberdashery. I was having a paranoid fit. Everybody knew. But moments later I walked proudly out into the street of Washington wearing my prize at a jaunty angle, the most beautiful snap-brim I'd ever seen.

The sun climbed high, warming through my overcoat, woolen suit and long red underwear as I headed for my appointment with J. Edgar Hoover. John Kennedy was President-elect; everywhere was the feeling of new life. I could smell the ozone, the euphoria of the nation's New Frontier, and as I walked, warmed by the sun and the excitement and vitality of a new city, for one brief moment I did see Washington as Camelot.

A store-window clock told me I had but half an hour before I was due at the New Agents' Class in the Justice building—which I knew lay ahead of me but I wasn't quite sure how far. A cab would have been the easy way, but new agents have to provide their own transportation to Washington, and after the air fare and a new suit of clothes my savings were nearly depleted. Besides I always enjoyed walking. And moments later, as I neared 9th Street on Pennsylvania Avenue the federal triangle rose before me, a portrait in chill austerity.

At the very apex arose granite walls a little whiter, a little brighter than those surrounding. Unquestioned, the Justice building dominated the landscape, the perfect repository for truth and justice. A wave of freshness swept overhead as I drew near, brightening even the antique cobblestones at my feet. I was humbled, but felt a surge of pride at being selected to play some part, a stone in the mortar of this great and powerful edifice to freedom.

Somehow I accomplished the impossible task of engineering my luggage through the massive revolving doors. The marble floor smiled back at me with my own face, my leather heels made sharp self-conscious echoes as I sought my way down the wide immaculate hallway toward 5231, the classroom assigned to the New Agents' Class. My career was about to begin.

I paused before the door and shifted the suitcase into my left hand. Even as I moved to open it the door swung outward and a man in a blue serge suit stepped briskly out into the hallway. He wore shiny steel-framed glasses and held a clipboard under one arm. His eyes jumped from my snap-brim to my suitcase as I stepped out of his way. "Looking for NAC?" he asked mechanically. The tone of voice was familiar.

"Yes, sir, I am."

"Your name?" He pulled the clipboard from under his arm and flipped past the top few pages.

"Ollestad . . . sir. Norman Ollestad."

He searched his list and when he found my name I would
have sworn he smiled, but to this day I can't be sure.

"Just step inside, Mr. *Ollestad*. Am I pronouncing your
name correctly?"

I fumbled with my suitcase. "Yes, sir. People are always
mispronouncing it but you're . . ."

"Fine," he interjected. "My name is George Keady. I am
to be your administrator while you are here at NAC." He
gave me a mechanical handshake. "Put your suitcase in the
corner and find your seat on the chart at the front of the
room. I'll be with you in a moment," he said, glancing at his
watch. "It is now eight fifty-five. Class will begin precisely
at nine."

He turned on his heel and clicked off down the corridor.
I watched as he disappeared into the men's room. I was
puzzled. His entire manner . . . the tone of voice was familiar.
Then I remembered. It was just like that of the agent, James
Fitzpatrick, who had interviewed me in Los Angeles.

Inside, the class was scattered about in groups, talking
quietly. There were about twenty men. As I entered, they
all turned toward me, plainly anticipating Keady's return.
Some smiled awkwardly, the others resumed talking. The
first thing I noticed was that everyone was older than I. I was
twenty-five, but they were almost all in their thirties, and
one man looked to be over forty. I wandered toward the
rear of the room where several suitcases were stacked, setting
mine down among them. Then I looked around for the
seating chart Keady had referred to. A wooden podium
stood conspicuously on an elevated platform toward the
front, flanked on either side by the stars and stripes. On one
wall hung a framed replica of the Justice Department seal.
So this was it. Within these four walls I would become an
agent of the F.B.I.

The chart was where the administrator said it would be and I found my seat in the front row. A husky fellow in his late twenties sat next to me; he nodded as I sat down. I was relieved to see someone near my own age. In a moment Keady walked briskly to the podium and our training began.

Special Agent George Keady, administrator of NAC, placed his clipboard and a sheaf of notes neatly to one side of the podium, then stood gazing from one face to another. We waited. Only after a few moments was it apparent that he was visually checking his seating chart against the twenty-two men before him. But the man didn't quite live up to the image of what I thought the ideal agent should look like. In fact, I thought he looked slightly ill at ease. Nervous. A big man with steel-rimmed glasses and close-cropped hair and a face which was almost too symmetrical. He reminded me of a worried Clark Kent, who had inadvertently wandered in, in search of a phone booth. The idea amused me, and as I smiled his steely gaze fell directly upon me. When he finally spoke the words came slowly.

"Gentlemen. After you have been with the Bureau for twenty years . . . you can retire." He paused for a full minute, collecting his thoughts it seemed. The class shifted nervously. We were eager; talk of retirement had left us confused . . . when we had yet to begin.

Once Keady got underway though his manner changed; he was more fraternal than he was our administrator. The mechanical precision of his words vanished, only the staccato rhythm remained. "Fellows," he addressed us with a friendly smile, "the Bureau retirement program is the best of any federal agency, bar none. It might interest you to know that a good many agents, at the age of fifty, are making in the neighborhood of eight thousand dollars annually—and that's *after* they've left the Bureau. While you are here the medical and life insurance programs are something you should take full advantage of . . . while you've still got plenty of lead in the old pencil." He looked up. Somebody in back of me let out a forced laugh. "And today we'll spend awhile talking about *Benefits of the Bureau. . . .*"

Two hours later, his lecture dragged to its sleepy conclusion. Keady pulled a stack of pamphlets from his clipboard, removing the rubber band that bound them, and walked down among us to distribute them. "Now, fellows, here you'll find everything you'll need to know about the various benefits and insurance programs. You will be pleased to note that the Director himself initiated many of them. It is through his personal efforts that we in the Bureau are able to enjoy these advantages. When the time comes for you to decide which programs to join keep in mind those to which the Director himself subscribes."

He continued passing out pamphlets, talking as he worked his way toward the front of the room where I was seated. Keady stretched across the row next to me and handed me the last pamphlet, and as he did the lapel of his obviously expensive, but ill-tailored suit bulged, revealing a thin, blue clip-on tie whose center was embossed with a handsome, leaping stag, the scene frozen in stately arabesque. Waves of blue serge billowed and spread like swells to distant shores, only to disappear as he straightened to face us. "That's all for now," he announced. "Take a twenty minute break. When you return you'll be addressed by Special Agent Frank Nash, assistant to the head of Training and Inspection Division."

The class broke for the door, relief plainly written on their faces. I was the last one out the door. It closed silently behind me. Out in the hallway everyone shuffled about nervously, lighting cigarets. That ought to cut their wind when the going gets rough, I thought. A dignified man in an expensively tailored suit walked by carrying a leather attache case. Everyone stopped talking, watching as he passed. I guessed he was a diplomat.

"That's one of the Justice Department attorneys." The voice startled me, and noting my surprise its owner smiled and moved across the hallway toward me. It was the fellow who sat next to me. He extended his hand. "My name's Bill Bruns," he said.

We shook hands and I introduced myself. He offered a cigaret. I declined and he lit one for himself, blowing a cloud of bluish smoke into the air above us. "You know, Ollestad," he said, "that fellow—the attorney who just walked by—makes less money than you do."

"Haven't earned a dime yet," I said.

"Yes, but you will. At seventy-nine hundred a year you'll be making almost a hundred a month more than him. And he's been on the job here for ten years. I'll tell you, Ollestad, we agents have got it made."

Bruns continued with his own, rather convincing version of the "Benefits of the Bureau," and I listened, fascinated by what he had to say. This man was the perfect F.B.I.-agent-prototype. Six feet tall and rugged. Like a wild-west hero, I thought. Somebody you wouldn't want to get into a gunfight with. Except for a few flaws in his English, he spoke intelligently. He was sharp, although he'd never been to law school like most of us . . . but he *had* been an F.B.I. clerk for more than three years before deciding to become an agent.

We exchanged personal biographies for the next fifteen

minutes. Then I excused myself and made a quick trip to the men's room. As I stepped inside the door and went about my business I heard rapid footsteps clicking down the hall outside. The door burst open behind me. I glanced into the mirror. A breathless George Keady stood in the doorway. Our eyes met for an instant. There was an urgency about him, and I expected him to dash for the nearest urinal, but he didn't. He just strolled over to the basin and soaped his hands as if nothing had happened.

I was mystified. Keady made an obvious display of washing and drying his hands and cleaning his nails and combing his hair until I walked out the door. The whole time he never said one word. It was some weeks before I found the reason for the administrator's strange behavior in the lavatory.

I hurried down the corridor to the classroom, planning to mention my strange encounter to Bruns, but when I got there I saw the speaker was already on the platform, hovering over the podium and thumbing through a ream of typewritten notes. From my front-row seat I took a good look at him. He was a big man with thick unruly hair and a heavy beard, the kind that never looks cleanly shaven. A mottled complexion only added to his dark demeanor, reminding me of someone—a character in the Canterbury Tales. The "Summoner," that's who it was. "Of whose visage children were afraid," was the only quote that came to mind, but it seemed to suit him. At least the thought amused me, although at the time I had no idea how ironic it really was. Indeed, his dark eyes flashed among us and it grew plain that before us stood a powerful man.

"Gentlemen, I'm Special Agent Frank Nash." He moved from behind the podium and stood before us quite at ease, passing a bit of white chalk from one hand to the other as he spoke. "My job here is assistant to the head of Training and Inspection Division. And I've come here today to tell you something of our Bureau."

He paused momentarily as Keady entered softly and took a chair by the door. Nash nodded without smiling and turned to the blackboard, where he wrote the words "Annuit Coeptis" in bold letters. Returning to the podium, he glanced down at the seating chart. "Mister . . . Robinson."

New Agent Thomas Robinson rose slowly and uncertainly from his seat. "How do you do, Mister Robinson," said Nash. "What is it I have written?"

"Annuit Coeptis," said Robinson, automatically pronouncing the C soft, like an S, and ignoring the O completely, so that Coeptis came out like Septis. I wasn't sure that was right.

The new agent was in his middle thirties, but his was a little boy's face. It was in keeping with his chubby physique, though incongruous with his fast-receding hairline. Right now he looked worried. Nash looked him full in his youngish face. "Come, come Robinson. You've pronounced it quite correctly, but what does it mean?"

A blank stare betrayed the new agent's bewilderment. Before he had the opportunity to compound his embarrassment Nash moved on down the chart. "Mister Ollestad." I rose to attention. Nash looked at me boldly, rather haughtily I thought. He nodded in my direction. "Perhaps Mister Ollestad can tell us the meaning of Annuit Coeptis." He walked to the front of the speaking platform and with his hands clasped behind him, glared down directly at me.

I feigned self-confidence. "I have seen it many times on our one-dollar bills . . ." That was as far as I got. Nash saw I was bluffing.

"That's right, Ollestad." His eyes scanned the faces of all twenty-two new agents at once. "Who knows the meaning?"

I glanced over at Bruns. He smiled faintly in my direction and shrugged his shoulders as if he didn't know either.

It took me completely by surprise when he rose to his feet, and spoke in a loud clear voice. "It means God looks with favor upon our work." Without moving his eyes from Nash's face, Bruns sat down.

That's right, I said to myself. Bruns was a former clerk; he should have known the answer.

"Correct," said Nash. "Mister Bruns is quite correct." He grinned at Bruns, who remained poker-faced. He looked out over the class again. "But some of you look puzzled. Come on, out with it. Doesn't seem to have much to do with a government bureau such as ours, does it?" He paused as if to gather momentum and then dropped his eyes to the podium where he shuffled through some papers, found what he was looking for, and then launched into his oratory with a full head of steam.

"Gentlemen, God does look with favor upon the work of the F.B.I. as protectors of this the greatest nation the world has ever known. Quite simply, this nation's problems are our own. . . ." Nash continued, his speech was mechanical and well rehearsed. Obviously he had been through the same dull lecture countless times before. He picked up a mimeographed sheet from the podium. "Here, let me quote for a minute from the Director.

'Today our country faces the most severe test ever to confront a free people. Here and abroad mortal enemies of freedom and deniers of God conspire to undermine the fundamental forces which are the lifeline of our country's vitality and greatness, our most formidable weapons in peace and war. These are Faith, Individualism, Courage, Integrity, and Discipline.' ' "

The class stirred restlessly. Nash paused and shot a hot look toward the back of the room. He flipped over the seating chart with his left hand. "I see you're about to raise your hand, Mister Rettis . . ." Rettis blanched. "I haven't answered the original question, have I?" Tom Rettis smiled meekly and nodded.

"Well, Rettis, this goes for you and everyone else in this room. As you look to your future, both in the Bureau and in your own personal life, never lose sight of the important lessons of the past. The world remains free only because a handful of courageous individuals—men of true faith, integrity, and discipline—have vigilantly patrolled America's most vital outposts for more than one hundred eighty years. *They* are the keys to democracy. Without them the gate to freedom must be forever locked. It is we who must endeavor to preserve the fluid pioneer spirit which, since our nation's conception, has contained the very essence of the American soul. Now there are those among us who would cast off our freedoms through neglect and abuse. The F.B.I. agent never hesitates to speak out, to bring public pressure to bear upon the negative influences of his community. He must never become so accustomed to filth, so intimidated by the advocates of a so-called 'worldly reality' that he fails to see corruption and decay as they really are."

Nash let the mimeographed sheet fall back to the podium, then edged forward, closer to his audience, assuming an informal manner.

His voice grew low, his dark eyes flashed among us causing not a few to stir uneasily. "But we in the Bureau are realists. We know that faith in its original simplicity will never be restored. The scientific intellect has drawn us too far too fast. The liberal . . . *intellectual* may have grounds for deploring certain conditions in our land today. But I submit that although conditions are not always ideal they are nevertheless true reflections of the Christian principles that gave them birth. We must never sell short man's ability to control his destiny through his divine relationship with God . . ."

The assistant to the head of the Inspection and Training Division paused, giving impact to his words. He was a skilled performer.

A clenched fist, a subtle change of inflection, an almost imperceptible tightening around the mouth—and he conveyed a world of meaning. Now his eyes shot toward the back of the room again. "Think we're a bunch of Holy Rollers, don't you Rettis?" Tom Rettis fidgeted with his hands and only stared. That was precisely what he had been thinking. Nash had him pegged, and he knew it. "Don't you Rettis!" he fairly shouted. Then his ugly plastic face contorted into an huge grin. He laughed. And the entire class laughed, hilariously, insanely, like puppets, at the end of a single string, and I laughed right along with them. We were all relieved at the most fortunate outcome of a potentially disastrous situation.

"Now, Mister Rettis. . . ." He waited for the class to calm down. Rettis tensed. "Mister Rettis, I'm finally going to get off your back." He flashed a fatherly smile, and the new agent let out an almost audible sigh of gratitude. "And believe it or not, I'm going to answer the original question. Indeed, what *does* Annuit Coeptis have to do with our government, with the Federal Bureau of Investigation?" The class was so quiet I could hear my own breathing.

Nash marched back and forth between the two flags mark-
ing the perimeter of his stage, and as he did I noticed he
wore the same ill tailored suit as Keady, the kind that with
each step his trousers flopped down over his shoes. We
watched for the rest of the afternoon as Nash quite dramatically framed the answer to his question.

Toward six o'clock his portrait was complete. "Annuit
Coeptis," his voice boomed, and he clenched both fists for
emphasis. "Indeed, God does look with favor upon the toils
of America. Don't ever forget that the Bureau is associated
in the public mind with the old fashioned virtues that have
made this country great. And it is these virtues that each of
you must hold as an individual, as an agent of the Federal
Bureau of Investigation. God looks with favor upon *our*
work. *Your* work. And believe me, the Bureau demands a
great deal from you. You will work. . . ."

Nash returned to the podium. "In the field, gentlemen,
your official hours will be from eight-fifteen to five . . . but
of course you'll work until eight every night. Here at the
Academy your hours are from nine to six. We start you off
easy." Once more he paused for dramatic effect, then dropped
his voice to a barely audible whisper. "You are excused."

I grabbed my suitcase and walked out into the hallway
with Bruns. Neither of us spoke. I cleared my throat, prepared to break the silence. Bruns was lost in thought. I saw
my shoes lusterless against sparkling marble and resolved to
shine them right away. The building still overwhelmed me.
I would have sworn somebody had painted the walls again
while we were in class.

In a moment we approached the massive revolving doors,
and I realized that after I passed through them I had no
place to go. I pulled the "approved housing list" from my

coat pocket with my free hand. Bruns followed me through the door. "Where are you going to be staying, Norm?"

"You've been around here awhile. Thought you might have some ideas," I said.

"Why don't you come on over to the Roosevelt, that's where I am. In fact, you can stay with me. I've got plenty of room. . . ."

I fumbled with the list. "Hey," he said laughing. "Put the damned thing away."

"But the Roosevelt's not listed," I said innocently.

"Don't sweat the list. You don't want to have anything to do with the Bureau housing over on East Capitol." We stopped walking and Bruns grew serious. "Look, Norm, I happen to know that a lot of agents stay there from time to time. Keady won't have anything to say against it. Besides, you'd like it there." He was smiling again. "It's closer to Georgetown, my friend. And the parties!"

# 4

That evening I moved in with Bruns, feeling no small amount of guilt at my first breach of Bureau discipline.

The Roosevelt stood on Sixteenth and V, behind a circular drive where a platoon of uniformed bellboys stood always at the ready. The imposing brownish building had obviously seen better days. Its management did their best to keep up appearances. There was a bar and a dining room, and the lobby was nicely furnished, but somehow its carpeting was always on the verge of looking soiled.

I remember someone had once told me a hotel could be judged by the class of prostitutes who hung around the hotel bar. The idea always amused me, but it was certainly true of the Roosevelt. Indeed, its well-dressed, well made-up women did their best to keep up appearances . . . but it was plain that they too had seen better days.

It was the same story all up and down Sixteenth. Many of the Washington embassies, as Bruns pointed out, were then, or had been in the past, located on Sixteenth. And in fact the Russian embassy stood right across the street from the Roosevelt, a source of constant jokes between us. V Street, however, was a different story. I walked down V by mistake one evening and ran into the worst slums I'd ever seen, only a block from the Roosevelt.

Our room at the Roosevelt was small, more convenient than it was comfortable. Bruns made a deal with the manager and we got a special monthly rate. It wasn't far to the Justice building, only fifteen minutes or so by bus. Occasionally we walked, and then it took nearly an hour. Up by seven each morning, we caught the seven-forty bus down Sixteenth, which dropped us within blocks of the Justice building.

Right across from "Justice," as everyone called it, was a plush, modern cafeteria that served fresh fruit, even in the dead of winter. Each morning found us over a leisurely breakfast at the cafeteria. Toward nine we strolled across the street to class.

On Tuesday, Keady's lecture was a general one. He explained that we would be tested frequently; that any new agent whose grade average fell below a B would be immediately drummed out of the class and out of the Bureau.

In the following days, as our training progressed, it would grow clear that Keady was really quite concerned for us all and that he himself would work very hard to shield us from such a terrible fate. As he lectured, "important" bits of information were prefaced by a sly wink. "You'd better write this down, fellows," he would say. "You might be seeing this again." And indeed we did. Our administrator gave us the test answers in advance word for word.

Toward the end of the day's lecture, Keady closed his notebook and walked down among us. He leaned back against an empty desk. "Boys, we'll be seeing a lot of each other the next thirteen weeks. I hope you'll listen closely to the advice you're given here in class. When you graduate you will be assigned to one of the fifty-seven F.B.I. field offices spread throughout the continental U.S. and its possessions. And from that first day forward, from the moment you report for duty you will be expected to discharge all duties in the manner expected of experienced agents." Now we experienced one of Keady's rare moments of enthusiasm. He wet his lips. His eyes glowed with excitement. "And I mean all duties," he said. "Including arrests, raids, the acquisition of latent finger prints . . . you must know how to conduct surveillances properly; you must educate yourselves in both practical technique and formal procedure. . . ."

But after that teaser we were sadly disappointed. Arrests, raids—the promises of practical application would not be realized. Not for awhile. Only the advice was forthcoming. For the remainder of our first week Keady outlined and re-outlined the Bureau rules for personal conduct. And twenty-two new agents, most of them long out of their teens and well into their thirties were lectured against the evils of drinking and gambling and stock-market speculation.

Wednesday and Thursday dragged by. Toward the end of class on Friday, Keady stepped down among us. Another round of advice, I figured. I glanced at Bruns. He was dozing. Several other members of the class were, too. But Keady never noticed. He seemed intent on what he was about to say. He began slowly. "Fellows . . ." He paused. "Today . . . before I dismiss you for the weekend, I would like to say a few words about . . . *women.*"

The class stirred to life. I expected Bruns to revive, too, but he didn't. He yawned as Keady stood collecting his thoughts, and whispered, "This ought to be good. . . ." And then as a second thought, he added in a more serious tone, "But don't let him shake you up."

For a moment I was completely mystified. But slowly I began to understand as Keady delivered with great emphasis a whole battery of rules designed to protect us—not from the insidious plots of enemy agents but from the diabolical clutches of a far more dangerous game. I sat spellbound as our administrator's eyes bugged, the veins bulged from his neck, and for that moment Keady was a blue-nosed missionary.

"Parties and dances are the most dangerous situations," he said sternly. "The girls—and by the way, fellows, don't let their age fool you . . . the young ones are the cleverest, in my experience." He choked a little on that admission, then continued bravely. "Those girls will get you dancing. And when they find out you're in the F.B.I. they'll go right to work trying to find a way to get their hands on those good Bureau paychecks. They don't stop there, either. That's why we in the Bureau keep a strong weather-eye peeled for men with weakness for women. . . ."

Up until now everything had been okay. A little boring perhaps. But now, despite Bruns' comment I was getting worried. I'd never gone in much for drinking or gambling, and the stock market was as mysterious to me as outer space. But I did like girls.

Keady stumbled through the next half hour building his awkward case against the evils of women. And I'm sure we all felt a lot better when he took a deep breath and said, "Now a word about marriage. Of course, you understand that the Bureau must be notified before there can be any change in the marital status of one of its agents. That is, his fiancée must submit to a thorough investigation before she may be permitted to join the Bureau family as his wife. . . ." Keady strolled back to the speaker's platform, then turned to add, "Besides even if she is approved, an agent is forbidden to discuss anything of his work with anyone. Including his wife." Keady finished up by pointing out the splendid example of our Director, J. Edgar Hoover, who was himself a heroic celibate of some sixty-five years.

That was it. Our first week of class was over, and Bruns and I filed out into the chill November afternoon together. But when I brought up the subject of Keady's lecture on women, Bruns surprised me. He dismissed it with a wave of his hand.

But I wouldn't be put off that easily. "Well what about all these rules and regulations that Keady spent a whole week talking about, and which we're supposed to memorize? Nobody could ever stick to them. They're ridiculous."

I didn't know it at the time, but Bruns' attitude would prove to be my salvation. He was cool. "Look, Norm," he said slowly. "That's not the right attitude. Believe me, I know. Just be calm and don't make waves. Coast along and keep your mouth shut in class and everything will work out all right." And just to prove the point, on our way back to the Roosevelt Bruns made a point of getting the phone numbers of two young secretaries who sat beside us in the bus.

As we walked into the lobby, Bruns ran into a group of friends, several of whom had been clerks in his old office. I went over to the desk and checked for mail, but there wasn't any.

"Hey, Norm." It was Bruns. "Hey, come on. Let's grab a couple of beers."

"Oh, I don't really feel like it."

"Come on, we'll show you some of the local Washington hot spots!" Bruns seemed excited at the prospect.

"No, I've got some letters to get off," I said. And I really did. I'd suddenly realized the reason I hadn't gotten any mail was that I hadn't written anybody yet. Nobody knew where I was.

"Hey, now," said Bruns, grabbing hold of my shoulders with his huge paws. "It's Friday. The *weekend.* You know what that means, don't you? It's time to take off the badge and let your hair down." He broke into a huge grin. "Besides, I feel duty-bound to get you in shape for the party tonight."

"Party?" I asked uncertainly. "What party?"

"*Georgetown*," he said in a cryptic tone. He glanced at his watch. "Tell you what. I'll go easy on you this time. You go on upstairs and do your chores and we'll rendezvous back here at eight. In the bar. Okay?" And without waiting for an answer he was gone.

I knew it was nearly eight by the time I finished the letter to my dad, but it didn't bother me too much. I hadn't planned on going to the party anyway. There was plenty of class reading to be done, and it seemed like a good night to study awhile, and then go to bed early. But after ten minutes of trying to generate some enthusiasm for the F.B.I. Manual of Instruction I gave up.

I glanced at the clock. It was just after eight, and I knew Bruns would be there any moment, and the thought of him down there waiting made me feel guilty. I picked up the phone. At least I could leave a message for him at the bar. But according to the operator all downstairs telephones were out of order. I was still dressed, so I grabbed my snap-brim (I never went anywhere without it now) and headed downstairs to deliver my apologies in person.

Bruns wasn't there yet. The place was practically empty. A pair of over-dressed floozies sat in a darkened corner at the end of the bar and whispered over their tall drinks. I hung my overcoat and snap-brim on the rack and sat down at the bar, right in front of the television, and I wondered if Washington TV was any better than Los Angeles'. The bartender was engrossed in the eight o'clock news and took his time serving me. But that was all right because I wasn't thirsty. The government doesn't pay new agents for a month, so I didn't have much money left anyway.

I was perfectly content just watching the news, but suddenly the bartender was there beside me with his flashlight and I knew in an instant I should have kept my hat on. I pulled out my California driver's license to prove I was twenty-five but I could see he still didn't believe me. He looked relieved when all I ordered was a coke. After that he left me alone. In a few minutes the news went off and a terrible movie came on. I decided against asking him to change the channel. It was eight-thirty and still no Bruns.

My mind wandered back over the past week of class. The whole thing had been pretty confusing. Then a crazy idea flashed through my mind. There was nothing keeping me. When you came right down to it nothing prevented me from grabbing the first plane home. I could be there by morning. Right then I wanted to go surfing more than I ever had before. And a life of surf-chasing up and down the coast didn't sound so bad at all. Malibu in the summer, Santa Cruz in the winter. Even a trip to Hawaii each January when the really big ones rolled in. Then after a few years, maybe I'd go back to law . . .

Suddenly I felt someone beside me and I looked up into the haggard face of one of the floozies from over in the corner, and I remembered the law partners and their cocktail party and the terrible women in capri-pants. Her red-rimmed eyes bore straight into mine without flinching. I was speechless. She turned to the bartender. "Got change for the cigaret machine?" The voice was crusty, she had a bad cold. I didn't feel like catching it. Digging into her huge purse, she finally came up with a dollar bill in one hand, a Kleenex in the other. The bartender got her change. Her eyes shot back into mine as she blew her nose hard and got up to leave. "If you're lonesome why don't you come on over and buy us a drink?"

I smiled a little nervously, shaking my head. "I'm waiting for a friend," I said.

Her mouth made a loose grin. "Well the invitation's still open, honey." I watched as she glided none too smoothly toward her table. But that wasn't the end of it. As I started in on my second coke, they were joined by four friends who made the first pair look like queens. There wasn't enough room so they moved to a large table right behind me. The bartender served them, and I couldn't help overhearing as they talked to him excitedly about the parties that were going on around town over the weekend. When he went to serve a new customer, their conversation turned to business.

Plainly, they enjoyed their work. They chattered back and forth about their various "tricks," and when two of them discovered they'd been out with the same customer only the week before they laughed so hard comparing notes on the poor fellow that one rushed off to the ladies' room for relief. While she was gone they unanimously agreed that Washington was generally the most prolific "hunting grounds," though two of their number were leaving for Miami the following Monday. Apparently they found the winter vacation season pretty good pickings in Miami too. One of them cracked a bad joke. Something like "When it's cold up North the heat's on down South . . ." Which really broke them up.

And as she returned from the restroom, the hooker gave me a bold leer, and then turned away as she saw I wasn't having any. They repeated the joke for her benefit, and after the laughter subsided she cocked her head in my direction and cracked "Yeh . . . and speaking of the heat . . ." They

all turned to stare at me, as I made a lengthy perusal of the
ice in the bottom of my empty coke glass. I guess I still had
something to learn about surveillance.

A few minutes later a tall, well-dressed fellow entered the
bar. He glanced about the room, then walked quickly over
to their table. They quieted and greeted him very politely.
He smiled amiably. They spoke for awhile, their voices
hushed. And soon all six got up and walked out the door;
he stayed behind and paid their check, then he too was gone.
I turned and watched through the window as they all got
into a waiting limousine and disappeared into the night.

Chuckling to myself, I thought back over their conversation. They thought they were really living as they jumped
back and forth from coast to coast, following the parties and
the *wheels* from Washington to Miami, and being swept up
by the big men in their limousines. But I thought they were
stupid; chasing the big boys would never get them anywhere.
Then I thought of my buddies in California, chasing the
surf up and down the coast and to Hawaii in the winter.
That was stupid, too. Where would it ever get them? Where
would surfing ever get me? That was just another escape, too.
Like the whores, afraid to face what they really were.

More determined than ever I grabbed my hat and over-
coat, prepared for another grim session with the Manual of
Instruction. I walked through the doorway and smack into
Bruns, whom I'd completely forgotten.

"Why you're right on time, old buddy," he said, ignoring
my obvious bewilderment. "The party's just beginning."

He had already steered me outside by the time I had a
chance to protest. But he would hear none of it. "Now I've
been around a little longer than you, Norm, and I know
damn well what's happening in this man's Bureau. I had to

learn the hard way. Now think about it. You are here on your first weekend in Washington and you want to curl up in bed with the Manual, of all things. Well, I'm here to tell you that's not the right thing to do at all. I can promise you'll learn a hundred times more about the Bureau at this party we're going to than you'll ever get from any book. If only by contrast."

I wasn't sure what he meant. But somehow, fifteen minutes later we were dismounting from the Georgetown bus, into a totally different world. Cobblestone streets crept uphill and downhill in all directions between hedgerows of tightly nestled brick and wood-framed houses. Well kept but unpretentious and carefully unmodernized, they stood much as they were a century before. Its people, as Bill told me, were an incongruous mixture of aristocracy and bohemians. Even the Kennedys had lived here before the White House. But then there was also that faceless mass of government employees that lived here, filled with a frenetic *joie de vivre*, and considered themselves swingers.

It couldn't have been much past nine-thirty, on a Friday evening, yet the town was stone silent. We crept through the cobblestone maze in silence, like men of the Yard tracking down some heinous criminal like Jack the Ripper. We stopped before a dimly lit frame house.

"This is it," he informed me.

The street was lined with cars. "Where are we?" I asked. "I'm completely lost."

"Good," he laughed. "But just in case I'm captured we're on 28th Street and Q Northwest." He led us around the side of the house to a rickety staircase, where a naked bulb burned at the head of the stairs. We started up. The railing creaked as I braced myself against it. The stairs sagged beneath my feet. I pictured myself plummeting to earth in a snap-brim and overcoat. I could see the headlines in the paper and the worried look on George Keady's face when he got the news.

We reached the top of the stairs. Bruns paused in front of the door, then turned to me. From inside came the thunderous opening of Beethoven's Fifth Symphony. "Sounds interesting," I offered.

"Oh, it'll be interesting all right," he said softly. "But don't be surprised at the reaction you get when people find out you work for the Bureau. Most of them will be government employees, too, but they. . . ." The rest of his sentence was forever lost as the door swung inward and a willowy girl with long dark hair that hung to her waist stood in the doorway. She smiled, gazing first at Bruns, then at me. We stared back, and for a moment no one said anything. Beethoven blared.

She was draped in a well worn, black wool sweater, several sizes too large. Skin-tight corduroy pants clung desperately to her long legs, which were swallowed up by a gigantic pair of blinding red patent leather boots. She held a drink in one hand, the other clung delicately to the doorknob as she swayed toward Bruns and spoke softly with a cultured New England accent. "Welcome, monsieurs, I am here to please you." Her eyes crinkled up in the corners. "Just give me the plans for the bomb!"

Bruns bent down to make a clown's play of kissing her hand, and when he arose he flipped out his badge and snapped into a wild-west gunfighting pose. "Don't move, Mata Hari, it's the F.B.I.!"

"How utterly charming," she cooed, beckoning for us to follow her inside. We were led to the bar where she poured us each a large cup of steaming red wine. I seldom drank, but the wine was hot and well spiced with cinnamon and slices of orange and lemon, and it did taste good, especially after our walk through Georgetown. I turned to appraise my surroundings. The bar divided the long, handsomely paneled room into two sections. Close to the door a dozen or more ascetic types were clustered about a dimly lighted table where they talked rapidly, sipping their wine. The other half of the room was pitch black. They seemed absorbed in their conversation, but as I stood there I noticed that every now and then one or another of them would glance furtively into the darkened corner where there was no light, where only the fireplace glowed, drawing silhouettes of lovers.

The record ended and a white-faced girl dressed all in black got up to change it. She saw me and smiled boldly. Suddenly it dawned on me. I stood there by the bar alone. And I turned just in time to catch a glimpse of Bruns and the girl as they faded into the cherry darkness. To stoke the fires, I guessed. I was on my own.

The music began again softly. And for a moment it took me back to Malibu where a group of us used to sit in the sand after school with the record player in the house turned up as loud as it would go, where we discussed politics and any number of terrible fates likely to befall the world if it continued on its present course, as college kids of all generations inevitably do.

"Do you like Beethoven?" The voice came from behind me. It was the girl in black. She was propped against the bar. Apparently she had been watching me for the last few minutes.

"I didn't see you there," I said.

"I know. You were listening to the music. But you *do* like Beethoven, then, don't you?" she asked hopefully. She cocked her head as the main theme appeared and the music began building toward a false crescendo. "Know what that means in Morse code?" she asked abruptly. Her eyes brimmed with knowledge.

"Doesn't everybody?" I said casually.

"Nobody here this evening has yet," she said. She sounded disgusted. "And I'll bet you don't either."

"Ever hear of Winston Churchill?" I ventured.

"Of course. But what's he got to do with Beethoven's Fifth Symphony?"

"He started the whole thing," I said teasing her. "Everybody knows that."

"Started what?" she said impatiently. "In case you didn't know, Beethoven and Churchill were more than fifty years apart. Beethoven died in 1827," she added knowledgeably.

"Well, Beethoven knew nothing of Morse code . . . but then Samuel Morse knew even less about Beethoven. Winston Churchill, however . . . well, he knew a good thing when he heard it. It was he who made that famous V for victory with his fingers during the Second World War and had them play Beethoven's Fifth, because first of all it sounded good, and then because the theme spelled out the letter V in Morse code. He was quite a showman, that Churchill . . ."

Her mouth dropped open and she stared at me without a word. She was stunned. "You must be new here," she said. Her tone was different now. Quieter and more reserved. Over the next few hours I was to learn that she was not the only one who was easily impressed by useless and often inaccurate information. "My name's Nancy," she offered, holding out a slim pale hand. "I work over at *State*. And you?"

We shook hands and I introduced myself . . . and Bruns was right: When I told her I was with the F.B.I. her reaction was indeed surprising. At first she was incredulous. And then as she saw I was serious, she led me over to her friends and slowly and theatrically staged an elaborate introduction to each and every one of them. Only at the end did she mention I was with the Bureau. Their conversation halted, followed by an awkward silence as they appraised me.

Then a skinny fellow in his early thirties, wearing a beard and the thickest pair of lenses I'd ever seen, started in on me. He, like most of them, worked "over at State," which I had come to learn meant the State Department, just as one or two others worked "over at Commerce." I stood by silently as he let it be known that my starting salary was seventy-nine hundred dollars a year. Which was true. And that as a rookie I made more than the "talented and experienced" head of the Central American desk over at State. It was plain they were trying to bait me.

It was also quite obvious they considered themselves *intellectuals;* that they as employees of the executive branch of government were the brains behind the country, while we of the Bureau supplied the brawn. Most of the fellows struck me as dull and rather homely and wore their beards a little too proudly, advertising their membership in the intellectual avant garde. The girls, though, were more interesting. Intelligent ivy-league types from Radcliffe and Vassar, they too wore the uniform of the beat generation—the sandals and long straight hair, but as such they were almost attractive. Mysterious, in any event. But as one or another of them walked around the room, to the record player and the punch bowl, I noticed they all had huge legs—as if there had been an epidemic of elephantiasis or some other strange tropical disease that had left them deformed. And they wore no stockings. "Truck tires on sportscar bodies," as Bruns later described them.

As the minutes passed and it came clear to my nemesis from State that I wasn't going to rise to the bait, the conversation drifted onto other subjects. (Meanwhile, I had been abandoned by my lady in black; she now sat in the lap of a new arrival who sported not only a beard but a magnificent black mustache as well.) I listened as they expounded on civil rights, wild-eyed, pounding the table with tiny, ineffectual fists. How easily they might fall prey to subversive elements, I thought. It was a good thing there was an F.B.I. around to protect them. They were plainly helpless.

For the better part of an hour my mind wandered. Until suddenly I realized the conversation had taken a new turn without me. I stared across the table in disbelief, directly into the proud eyes of the girl named Nancy, as her mustachioed suitor quite dramatically compared the movement of Beethoven's symphonies to the rhythms of none other than my sport of riding the ocean's waves. Surfing. One after another they all took up the discussion, until half an hour later poor Beethoven had been cast aside and they had settled down to devour the sport's own psychological skeleton.

"The real reason so many have fallen prey to the fascinations of this sport," reasoned my friend with the heavy glasses, "is that in surfing there is a psychological exhilaration that comes from overcoming gravity and the other natural forces involved." He turned to Nancy and her beau. "Certainly, rhythm is basic not only to one man's music as some of us might like to believe, but to all of life itself. I submit that the surfing mystique is a specific function of the psychology of myth. Because the sport is an American product, its myth, too, must necessarily be a Christian one."

He turned toward the open-mouthed couple and delivered his coup de grace. "My friends, I have been to California.

And I have seen them with my own eyes. Like Christ, these surfers actually walk on water!"

I was dumbfounded. But before I could digest this last morsel the oval-bodied girl in black jumped to her feet, rallying in her own defense. Fire glinted in her eyes as she paced back and forth and spun her own delightful web. "The ocean," she explained clinically, "may be described metaphorically as the deep emotional water of our psyche. Just as riding a wave may be described as the act of love. . . ." Every one of her rapt audience was on the edge of his chair as she built toward the inevitable. "I see the surfboard as a phallus," she said quite seriously. "And when the wave breaks—*climax!*" Her face was flushed with abstract excitement.

No one even smiled. I could barely contain myself. Here, in the frigid wastes of Georgetown, a motley group of State Department beatniks was having more fun discussing the surf than any of us had ever had actually *riding* the waves at Malibu on a six-foot, glassy day. They were odd-balls all right. Widely read, though, and for the most part they did have good information on almost any topic that came up. But their degenerated bodies and their sick attitude toward life made them bystanders. Not one of them could have paddled out into a four-foot ocean swell, much less actually *surf* one. Because they were unable to participate they had become critics, abstracting, intellectualizing everything. They could *do* nothing.

It was nearly three in the morning when I noticed Bruns helping himself to the dregs of the punchbowl. The girl was nowhere in sight. He stood by my chair and drank the wine slowly, listening to my friend with the glasses as he argued with an extremely inarticulate but relatively good-looking girl about Toynbee's interpretations of history. When the fellow noticed Bruns listening, he flushed visibly and lost himself in mid-sentence. Apparently, something had gone on between them in the past for he called my room-mate by name.

"Well, Mister Bruns, I see you are smiling. Something we lowly clerks have said amuses the magnificent special agent of the F.B.I. Tell me, Bruns, what is it that makes you agents so *special* after all?"

Bruns took a final long draught of wine and set the empty cup down on the table. He smiled, looking the fellow straight in the eye as he spoke. "Well, my friend, I shouldn't have to tell you the answer to that one. You who are so knowledgeable when it comes to dates and places, when and where events have occurred in the past. It is history that has made the Bureau what it is today in the hearts and minds of the American people. Yes, history. What you fail to understand is that history is merely the biographies of our great men. And if for a single moment one of you believes that our Director, J. Edgar Hoover, is not truly a Carlyleian 'Man on Horseback,' you are sadly deluding yourself...." Bruns continued and from the expressions on their faces I could see that he could have had any one of the girls in that room. Quite obviously, a glib tongue was the key to success here in Georgetown.

In the weeks to follow, I worked up an approach of my own—one that involved a philosophical comparison between India's attitude toward the Portuguese colony of Goa and the historical position the United States had maintained toward Mexico's possessions in California. It was wild and full of holes. But it was esoteric and therefore it worked like a charm. Never again would I sit with the "intellectuals" at the Georgetown parties.

# 5

"All right, Ollestad, who'd you shack up with last weekend?"

The tone of voice was positive—as if my interviewer really expected an answer. What a way to begin the week, I thought. But then "Doc" always did begin his interviews with questions about my sex life. It was important to him. NAC was constantly being interviewed during training, once by every supervisor, assistant director and instructor in the Academy, but Doc just happened to have a degree in psychology, which helped explain his particular line of questioning. And with him each interview was an unforgettable experience.

"Are you kidding?" I replied innocently.

Doc had curly blond hair that clung down over his forehead like bleached ivy. Just a little too far, in fact, so you couldn't help staring at it, wondering if it were real. Right now he held his familiar pipe in his left hand, and I watched as the right hand roved aimlessly through his desk drawer in search of a match. When he occasionally did find one and lighted his pipe he invariably forgot about it and it went out, which caused the whole procedure to begin all over again. But he was actually a pretty smart fellow, and with his strange habits I thought of him as the Academy's absent-minded professor. The only objectionable thing about him was that he considered himself *cool*.

53

He looked at me blankly. "Are you kidding me?" I said, repeating myself. He still hadn't found a match.

Doc gave up and shut the drawer, staring at me rather quizzically. He had the habit of laughing and clearing his throat every other sentence. "Ha ha . . . ahem, look you think I'm not with it, don't you, Ollestad? Well, I know what goes on with you young agents. Ahem. We're experts in this type of investigation, you know." I nodded, trying to effect a blank expression. "Ha ha . . . as a matter of record we're kept busy twenty-four hours a day just watching our clerical and stenographic staffs. Why these young Southern belles get up here to the Seat of Government . . . and all they want is *sex!*" He shot a hard look. "Know what I mean, Ollestad?"

I nodded, smiling perhaps a little too much as I thought of Bruns and his Georgetown "Mata Hari." That little tale would have made the inspector's day.

Plainly, Doc was a man who enjoyed his work. He grinned broadly as he gathered together a half dozen typed sheets and handed them across the desk. "Think we're not *hep* to what's happening, Ollestad? Take a look at these," he said proudly. "Signed confessions. Wrung them out of three young flowers only yesterday. All of them F.B.I. clerks. The pride of Virginia . . . until this morning when they were *fired!*"

The phone on his desk buzzed softly. He picked it up and placed his hand over the receiver before answering. "Read them," he said. "They're *interesting.*" He leaned back in his chair and talked casually into the phone, and as he talked Doc puffed away on his still un-ignited pipe. And for a solid fifteen minutes I enjoyed a candid look at what made the Inspector tick.

It was Doc who last week had given us our tour of the
Justice building. Some class members who already knew their
way around Washington and the capitol complex had been
through before, on a tour designed for the public. And they
complained a little when ours turned out exactly the same;
but it was the first time for me and I was fascinated.

Doc led us slowly and dramatically through the basement
firing range and the exhibits sections, where we were held
captive by well documented displays of Bureau triumphs—
the execution of the Rosenbergs, John Dillinger . . . and all
the while his bearing was calm and self-assured, almost dignified.

But as we left the Bureau hall of fame and entered the
world famous F.B.I. laboratory Doc grew suddenly excited.
His forehead was damp, and the nervous laugh came more
frequently as he pointed out the bits and pieces of hands
and feet and swatches of hair that were to be analyzed for
identification processing. We passed by the remains of a
human body that had been stuffed inside a trunk, then deposited in a Philadelphia railroad station, where it remained
hidden for many months. Overhead, rows of bottles stood
like olives in the supermarket, but these contained the neatly
labeled fingertips of plane-crash victims which awaited
identification.

The lab was an efficient and impressive complex. And Doc
glowed as if it were a personal triumph all his own.

We were led into a room off the main lab, where a sickening stench hit all of us in a sudden blast of warm, moist air.
In one corner a grey-smocked technician was busy opening
freshly arrived packages of evidence. He stood aside as we
entered and wiped his brow. The smell was almost over-
powering now. Several of my classmates looked about nerv-

ously, obviously sickened. One of them froze, his eyes fixed on something in the center of the room. And there, on an aluminum table, lay the incredibly pale and emaciated body of a woman, awaiting dissection.

The stench and the ghoulish spectacle of the decaying corpse turned my stomach. I turned away noting that I was not alone. Indeed, New Agent Thomas Robinson was having a far worse time of it than I was. As Robinson slumped back against a sink, Doc's high-pitched voice all but shattered the new agent's nerves. "Look at this!" he exclaimed, gesturing toward the cadaver. Nobody moved. "Come on now, fellows. Gather 'round. No time to be shrinking violets. This isn't the high school prom—it's the F.B.I.!" The class edged closer, reluctantly. Robinson was immobile. His normal pallor had turned a sickly green.

Doc continued his detailed account of how the cadaver would be subjected to the most arduous and detailed analysis, failing in his fervor to notice Robinson, who stood alone now by the sink with his shoulders thrown back as they always were above a protruding pot belly.

Robinson was the one man in our class I could not see as a special agent of the F.B.I. I had finally gotten over the initial shock of the entire class's being older than I; and although they were all in terrible physical condition, save Bruns and myself, I figured the F.B.I. Academy at Quantico would whip them into shape soon enough. And, too, they must have had other redeeming qualities or the Bureau would not have hired them in the first place, I thought.

But for Robinson there was no hope. Not only was he weak physically, but the fact that even during our first few days of training he had run constantly to our administrator with all manner of classroom gossip irritated me. He was a stool-pigeon. And to make up for his inadequacies, he, among all of us tried the hardest to look, act, and dress like our instructors, as he spoke the clipped Bureau parlance, wore the same floppy suits and thin clip-on ties.

In class he had the annoying habit of absent-mindedly picking the blemishes that clustered about his pointed chin, but right then in the cadaver room of the F.B.I. laboratory all of the new agent's senses were alert. No boredom glazed his eyes; they jumped wildly, frantically from one thing to another in a desperate attempt to avoid all contact with the corpse. His nose twitched. And he pulled a neatly squared handkerchief from his breast pocket to mop the perspiration from his face.

As Doc turned in his direction Robinson mustered every ounce of his strength to look attentive and unaffected. "Now, fellows," said Doc, looking directly at Robinson, "please note that the skin seems to lose its elasticity after death." Doc pulled a pen from his coat pocket and pointed out an area under the corpse's chin where the skin clung in loose folds much like that of an iguana.

"Also note that the extremities swell . . . almost as if she'd been pumped full of air . . ." He laughed, coughed, then turned to the next exhibit—just in time to miss the spectacle of Robinson as his knees sagged and he vomited quietly into a convenient basin.

That's it, I said to myself. I'd figured Robinson would eventually disgrace the class. Any second Doc would turn around. But while Doc became quickly engrossed in one of his tiresome war-stories, Bruns leaped to the rescue. Towering over him as he did, Bruns completely hid the sickly Robinson from view. As if to pass a casual remark, he turned and slapped him sharply across the cheek, loudly clearing his throat simultaneously to disguise the sound. It worked! Robinson straightened up and without even so much as a look at Bruns, he marched straight out the door with the class, following Doc into the next room.

I stared after him, incredulous. Bruns ran some water into the basin, washing away all traces of the new agent's cowardice. "Why did you ever stick your neck out for him, Bill? You'd have really caught hell if Doc had seen you trying to hide something from him. He's a bug about things like that."

"How do you know Doc *didn't* see?" he snapped. "If Robinson had made a big thing about getting sick—if more than a few of us had seen him it would have been bad for all of us." He dried his hands on a paper towel, and then we started off in pursuit of the class. I noted the lab technician was smiling as we left. Had *he* seen, too? Bruns continued: "Norm, you've got a lot to learn about the Bureau. A lot that's useless to even tell you because you wouldn't understand. Not until you get out into the field. But you'll find out that the world is full of Tom Robinsons. Only out in the field there's always someone around to cover for them . . ."

*"You're not covering for anybody, are you, Ollestad?"* It was Doc. I still held the "confessions." As he took them from me, he looked me full in the face. I gazed back innocently as he coughed and continued the interview. "Come on, man, what have the other agents been up to?"

"Nothing I know of, sir," I replied.

"If you are covering for anybody. . . ." He paused, then changed his tack. "Hah . . . look, now, Ollestad, the stool-pigeon concept is a product of the underworld designed to thwart law-enforcement. As an agent of the F.B.I. you have an obligation to fill me in on the goings-on of your fellow agents. I know there's hanky-panky going on. There always is. And I'll get to the bottom of it!" he exclaimed suddenly, slamming his fist down on the desk. He leaned across the desk and continued quietly "Look, Ollestad, don't worry about yourself. I *know you're* all right."

He smiled and I thought he was going to reach over and pat me on the shoulder, as he said, "Why, Ollestad, I've appraised you as *special agent in charge* material! What do you think of that?" He blustered right on without waiting for a reply. "But some of those guys in your class might be goof balls. And we're entitled to know about it. Come on, man, what's happening?" He was trying to get jazzy again.

Once more I protested our innocence. Doc glanced at his watch, and apparently satisfied I was telling the truth, he stood up signalling the end to our interview. I got up, we shook hands, and I started for the door.

"Uh . . . Ollestad? You will keep me posted, won't you?"

I'd have sworn I heard him sigh with relief when I reassured him that indeed I would keep him informed.

# 6

Indeed, as Bruns suggested, there was much that I might learn about the F.B.I. And as the days and weeks of training began to pass more quickly it came clear that our role, as Bruns described it, over other federal agencies (and even occasionally over local law enforcement agencies) was that of the "police who policed the police."

But curiously enough, the source of the Bureau's extraordinary reputation could not be attributed realistically to "those agents in blue" nor even to such singular agents as the "Georgia Cracker." No, the power behind the Federal Bureau of Investigation lay totally and irrevocably in the hands of a single man. The Director, J. Edgar Hoover.

Certainly I would have guessed it on my own, as day after day we were steeped in the law and lore of Bureau ritual. But the F.B.I. was never one for guesswork; though it did come as a total surprise when one day Keady stepped aside from the speaker's podium to make way for the men who had come to tell us the real story of the Director's incredible rise to power.

"Fellows," our administrator announced breathlessly, "I am pleased to introduce the first of today's two speakers, Special Agent Jess Doyle, assistant to the Director." He beamed as the tall thin agent, greying and in his late forties, stepped forward and slowly and meticulously organized his notes on the podium before him. A wave of new interest surged among us at the presence of someone so close to the Director. It was a long moment before he looked up.

Keady meanwhile made his way silently to the rear of the classroom where he took an empty seat beside the agent who I figured would be next to address us. Hushed, the class waited expectantly.

The assistant to the Director rose well over six feet tall, though the ill fitting charcoal suit he wore gave the impression of a much smaller man. Indeed, his slight frame was lost within it. The trousers were gathered loosely about his waist, secured as they were by a tightly cinched leather belt. There was a willowy bent to his shoulders as he perused his notes. The man's face was incredibly smooth. I wondered if he even shaved. And strangely his mouth opened almost too wide as he began speaking in his shrill but toneless voice.

"Boys," he began slowly, his eyes still cast down upon his notes, "as both your administrator and Inspector Nash have undoubtedly indicated in past lectures the Bureau is held in the highest esteem by the American people. Certainly, you were all aware of this before you joined the Bureau. . . ."

Doyle paused and glanced up. I hadn't noticed before but his eyes were so grey they were almost colorless.

"You see," he continued, "our reputation was not handed to us on a silver platter. Nothing could be farther from the truth. No, it was hard won by a single man. J. Edgar Hoover."

His eyes fled back to the podium, and he continued with the staccato cadence which by this time had grown more than familiar. "But I want to emphasize it would take only a single bad apple to spoil everything the Director has worked for. Which is the very reason for the Bureau rules and regu-

lations you have been required to memorize, and the obvious
necessity for the physical and moral discipline you will
undergo here in training . . ."

Half an hour later, Doyle looked up from his notes,
apparently through with his prepared speech. He seemed
more relaxed and his voice dropped an octave. "Now I'm
sure all of you would like to hear a little about the Director
himself, and how he built this Bureau from the ground up."
The class leaned forward in their seats. Even Bruns looked
interested.

"Well on August first, nineteen-nineteen, our Director first
became associated with the Bureau . . ." Doyle winked toward
the back of the room. "And boys, you just might see that
date again somewhere . . ." (Doyle, too, I mused.) "During
those dark days the Bureau was but the seedling of the great
American oak it is today. Its very life was in danger; the
Bureau was run by a bunch of ruthless and unscrupulous
characters. Looking back it is difficult to believe our Director
was only twenty-four years old at the time. Yes indeed," he
said seriously, "these were troubled times for the Director.
Youthful as he was, and surrounded by thieves, he was
tempted to resign in favor of entering private law practice.
Yes, the temptations must have been great. Most assuredly
had he done so he would be a very rich man today, what
with his tremendous talents. But no! The Director chose the
path of sacrifice; and electing to forego private wealth and
what to *lesser* men are the *pleasures* of life, he dedicated
himself instead to the creation of the organization we are
proud to serve today. Against all odds, our Director stuck
doggedly to his purpose; today he remains the guiding light
of the F.B.I.—in spite of liberal-leftist moves for his ouster.
. . ."

I was astounded. Who, I wondered, would ever want to remove such a paragon from office? And who were these liberal-leftists? What kind of *Americans* were they? Certainly, I thought, President Kennedy would never sit still for such a thing. And I put the thought quickly from my mind.

"Now, boys, let me give you a few of the facts about the early days of the Director's new and burgeoning F.B.I. On May tenth, 1924, Attorney General Stone offered him the job of acting director. (You'll be seeing that date again, boys.) The Director was then but twenty-nine years old. (That, too.) He gave his acceptance only under certain conditions: First, that he have full authority over hiring and firing Bureau personnel; second, that the Bureau be completely divorced from politics; and third, that appointment and promotion within the Bureau be placed exclusively on a merit basis. And of course these same conditions still exist today, even after forty years of service. Our Director has served thirteen attorney generals, has assisted seven presidents, and he still works longer hours than any of us, every day of the year. . . ." No wonder Doyle's face glowed with pride, I thought as he concluded. "Yes, boys, J. Edgar Hoover is an inspiration to us all. Indeed, it has been said, and truly —*'The sunshine of his presence lights our way!'* "

On that note we were given a twenty-minute break. And for the first time since NAC had begun, we were eager to get back to class. Up till now the Director had been but a powerful and fascinating myth. Now that myth was for the first time coming very much to life.

Apparently Doyle too was anxious to get underway; we filed back into the classroom and he began speaking even before we were settled in our seats. "I suppose most of you have wondered just how the Director has been able to rally such tremendous support, both from the American people and from their duly elected representatives in Congress," he said, clipping each word carefully as it fell.

"Well, as we all know, the center of American life is in the home, and following this principle the Director was quick to establish good relations between the Bureau and the towns and cities across the nation. For example, one of the Bureau's *unofficial* services to the community is our practice of providing businessmen with inside information about job applicants and about their current employees as well, if they request it. Which is a great help in keeping those bad apples out of their organizations. Employees whose questionable loyalties have been known to stand in the way of their respective companies receiving important military contracts. And believe me, the business community appreciates our help!

"At our bank robbery conferences, highly specialized agents lecture bank officials, instructing them in the latest methods of robbery prevention. Because the bank officials are already familiar with our operations they can lend far greater assistance when robberies do occur.

"And of course back in 1935 the Director established the National Academy as a forum to further communicate modern police methods to law enforcement officers on the local level. More than twenty-eight percent of the Academy graduates have climbed to such high positions as chief of police, sheriff, and state police chief. The advantages of a well trained local police force to the Bureau are obvious.

"Another important community aid is the Law Enforcement Bulletin, which, by this time, you have all seen. But did you know that each month *forty-eight thousand* copies are distributed? For years it has been an excellent vehicle for disseminating timely information on law enforcement. The contents of each issue are personally approved by the Director himself." Without raising his eyes from the podium, Doyle held a recent copy aloft so we all might see its handsome format.

He continued reading from his notes. "Here, in the latest issue our Director states: '. . . More than three hundred fifty years ago a small number of grateful pilgrims assembled in prayerful tribute to God for an abundant first harvest. That occasion marked the launching of a meaningful custom, which has become one of our nation's most cherished holidays—Thanksgiving Day!' "

Now Doyle's colorless eyes flashed down among us as he plunged home the point. "Everyone knows that Thanksgiving Day observance is not a federal law, nor is it within the scope of our Bureau's all too limited jurisdiction. But because of our Director's prestige, because of his reputation as *the* protector of American rights and freedoms, he has been able to comment upon them. And he is listened to! Which is something no other director of any federal agency can say. The Bureau is unique!"

The assistant to the Director reduced his shrill voice to its lowest, barely audible ebb. "Now, boys, books have been written criticizing our Director . . ." His nodding head expressed his incredulity. "But they are filled with nothing but contemptuous lies and half-truths . . . Communist style!"

The voice climbed higher and louder as his fervor grew. "They are an attempt of the Communist conspiracy to degrade us in the public eye! The *Commies* are well aware that if ever the support, cooperation, and allegiance of the American people were reduced, the Bureau would be greatly handicapped. For this reason our Director can never tolerate unjust, destructive criticism! If ever the public lost faith, law enforcement would suffer terribly . . . *and evil would most certainly triumph over God. . . .*" The thought was too much for him; strained to its upper limit the shrill voice began to crack. For a moment he was unable to speak. The wide mouth moved soundlessly.

Quickly, though, he regained control, and we all relaxed as he continued. "So in each F.B.I. field office one agent is designated to follow the press; to track down all references to the Bureau, and to notify the Director immediately upon even the slightest mention so the Director may compliment our supporters and set the record straight with our adversaries. *We are not afraid of the truth;* it is only backhanded, destructive criticism based upon erroneous information that we deplore. We rest confident that the Director, backed up by his facts and figures, will emerge victorious in any controversy.

"To combat false information, the Director has organized a full-time staff who work as public relations advisors. One such advisor was the well known radio and television announcer, Dan Smoot. But of course," Doyle was quick to add, "the Director always makes the final decisions.

"When the advisory staff learned that an inordinately high percentage of American intellectuals read the *National Geographic Magazine,* the Bureau managed to get an article into that publication telling the true story of the Bureau."

"In answer to the more specific assaults of his enemies, the Director arranged for a book to be written—which might sound like propaganda . . ." Doyle chuckled. His gaunt face brightened into a wry smile. Of course the idea was absurd. But Doyle amplified the statement. "What the Director desired was a truthful, accurate, and favorable account of the

Bureau's activities. One written by someone *outside* of the Bureau, to establish an objective viewpoint. And of course the book was ultimately quite successful: it answered all the Director's critics without it becoming necessary for the Director to speak out in his own defense.

"Which brings up another of the Director's virtues: he never honors his enemies with a direct reply. He stands silent amid the elements that would destroy him—adamant, like the Rock of Gibraltar. Whenever a reply does become necessary, the assistant to the Director, Earl T. Christman, or the Society of Former Special Agents of the F.B.I., or some other impartial outsider always leaps to his defense.

"The Director himself wrote a book about Communism a few years back, *Masters of Deceit,* which I am sure you have all read cover to cover. Hundreds of thousands of these precious volumes have been personally autographed by the Director and distributed to Americans in every walk of life. A master stroke!"

Doyle declared in his final assault, "Our Director has cast his bread upon the waters. And should ever the need arise it would return a thousand-fold. Every American patriot with such a powerful document on the shelf of his own home library can be counted on to stand up for the F.B.I.!"

Suddenly, almost abruptly Doyle's lecture was concluded. And we were excused for lunch.

Upon our return, the dark-complexioned agent who had sat at the back of the room with Keady during the morning's lecture was at the podium. Neither Keady nor Doyle was in sight. But indeed, Assistant Director William J. Dainard, as he introduced himself, was a different man. He spoke confidently, informally—almost as if he were one of us. Taller than Doyle, even huskier than Nash, the assistant director was a fine figure of a man. Distinguished. His dark chestnut hair greyed slightly at the temples. His grey flannel suit was impeccable and well tailored, and his black shoes were freshly shined. He smiled professionally.

"Gentlemen," he said and the deep, resonant voice reached every ear. It commanded attention, speaking to us not as a class but as individuals. "You may not realize it but you are in very select company. Only one man out of every six thousand that apply is accepted for F.B.I. training." His bright eyes, jumping from face to face, made instant contact. "Soon you will become one of the sixty-two hundred special agents of the F.B.I. Keep in mind that thirty-six million men applied for your jobs. And among them were both Robert Kennedy and Richard Nixon. Each was rejected! Kennedy because he was too cocky, Nixon because he wasn't aggressive enough. Now of course since that time both have risen to high government positions, and it is entirely possible that they might now make the grade. But at the time they applied, no.

"Now you might well ask 'How ever did the Bureau become so exclusive?' Well, gentlemen, today I am here to explain precisely how this has come about. And how the Director has led the Bureau to the high position it holds today."

Almost imperceptibly Dainard glanced down at the podium where a tiny 4 x 5 card contained his lecture notes. Without breaking rhythm he continued. "Now in 1924 he established the Identification and Records Section, which is the best system of its kind in the world. Prophetically, our Director rejected the Bertillon system of body measurement, basing his system instead on the one totally unalterable human characteristic—the fingerprint . . ."

The assistant director's lecture technique was actually

rather interesting, if a bit confusing at first. He balanced the dry bits and pieces of Bureau history with a colorful collection of exciting anecdotes drawn from his own twenty-year career with the F.B.I.

Concluding his spiel on the Identification and Records Section, Dainard shifted automatically. "Now, gentlemen," he said, "subsequent events have borne out the wisdom of the Director's choice. Several years ago a condemned man was cleared of an alleged crime, although his measurements were identical to those of the real criminal—*according to the Bertillon criteria.* But his fingerprints made him a free man!"

Now he assumed a confidential tone. "And incidentally, the man our Director saved was a *Negro.* Remember that if you ever happen to hear any talk of Bureau prejudice. We have *all* kinds—just like this great nation of ours, the Bureau is a melting pot. Check the list of division heads, which you will be required to memorize, and you'll find that a *Jew* is head of the General Investigations Division. . . ."

Occasionally, though, his digressions rambled so far afield that the original subject was never regained. Talk of Bureau prejudice, for example, seemed to put him on the defensive, and the Identification and Records Section was abandoned permanently.

"From time to time," he said seriously, "you may come in contact with critics of the Director—*Communists,* for the most part—who would undermine the integrity of the Bureau and the freedom of this great land. If ever they were to succeed in weakening this Bureau or in undermining our Director . . . well, the rest would be easy.

"But there are other sources of unwarranted criticism. The *liberals* in public office have great fear of our investigations. Doesn't it seem strange that they all have records of previous trouble? Another thing, gentlemen, many of these so-called liberals are actually *queers*. No wonder they are always the ones who yell the loudest about the Bureau's secret files. . . ."

Which of course led us to a brief side note on the Director's files. "Now the only reason in the world that those personal background files exist at all," he explained easily, "is to help prepare our Director for statements to the press. A single error might destroy our reputation. I'll give you an example. A number of years ago, Henry 'Red' Sanders, the famous U.C.L.A. football coach, died and a lot of famous people made emotionally inspired comments to the press about his 'greatness.' The Director had known Sanders, and when he was approached to do the same he refused. Why? Because the Bureau had an extensive background file on Sanders; and because of Sanders' immoral life the Director naturally declined to comment. You see, if we were not prepared with literally *millions* of such files the Bureau, placed in ignorant and embarrassing positions, would surely be torn to shreds by its enemies."

Dainard paused abruptly. I heard the sounds of the door at the rear of the classroom; it opened and closed again softly. The assistant director gazed toward the back of the room for a long moment before he spoke. His composure was slightly shaken.

Wondering who had come in, I turned and there in the last row, sitting straight and stiff and looking terribly nervous was our administrator, George Keady. His right eye twitched visibly. Beside him sat a heavily bejowled and greying man whom I thought I'd seen around the Justice Department before, but I couldn't place him.

"Gentlemen," said Dainard proudly, and the voice boomed louder than ever. "I would be derelict in my duty if at this point I did not pay tribute to the courageous agents who have dedicated themselves to the service of this Bureau . . . agents like Associate Director Christman, who I am proud to announce has joined us here today." Dainard nodded respectfully toward the rear of the class, as every new agent snapped instantly to attention, each to a man contemplating any number of imagined significances to this unexpected visit from the man closest to J. Edgar Hoover.

Without looking at his notes, Dainard continued. "Associate Director Christman has received many fine offers from private industry. He has been offered great sums for his demonstrated administrative talents—but he has chosen to stand loyally by our Director. . . ." His keen ear sensing the unctuosity of his own words, Dainard sought to spread it around a little. "Now this same quality of devotion is shared by the heads of *all* divisions—men who have been personally selected by our Director. Which is, of course, the greatest assurance that only the cream shall rise in the F.B.I., where only merit counts. Even politics' almighty sword has found the Bureau impregnable: The Director pays no heed to the political or religious beliefs of the men he picks for advancement. Never taking sides, he just performs his job as it is defined by Congress, leaving the quest for personal power to the politicians. . . ."

A rustling came from the rear. Dainard's head jerked in that direction. Was Christman going to speak? Tension filled the air. The door closed softly. Christman was gone. The class shifted in their seats and we all relaxed, and Dainard smiled down at us as we did. He glanced at his notes. "Gentlemen, let's learn more about the man who leads us!

Not enough mention can be made of him." The assistant director beamed like a Boy Scout who had just been awarded his eagle.

Over the next few hours Dainard alternately lectured and digressed, till finally toward the end of the day he wound up with a typically circuitous commentary on the Director's carefully conceived public relations strategy. "One of his great achievements was the disaster squad which has been in existence here at the Seat of Government ever since the tremendous boom in air travel began. Each member of the squad is an agent of a minimum five years' experience. Each has his passport and visas up to date for every peace-loving nation in the world. You can readily see how valuable this service is to insurance companies and to anyone concerned with the identity of crash victims. Although it is not what you would call a function strictly within our jurisdiction, it does have tremendous impact on public opinion."

Once again clouds of memory fogged his eyes. "Now as I mentioned earlier the Director goes to great lengths to mold public opinion about the more serious problems that plague our nation. No one is more aware of them than he. And so each year the Director issues statistics on local crime in major American cities. Not long ago, for example, he grew concerned over the tremendous upswing in the child-molestation category. Instructions were subsequently issued to the staff, and before long local police and parent-teacher groups were apprised of the situation. Simultaneously, the wheels were set in motion on our own Exhibits Section, which does all the Director's art work, and before long we were distributing posters warning children against talking to strangers. The Director even wrote an article in the Law Enforcement Bulletin. . . .

"And then," he whispered, "*I* discovered a new approach. One that was instantly approved by the Director, for as he has stated many times, 'An agent advances in the Bureau just as his counterparts in the business world: by the use of a free creative imagination, tempered by a sense of moral responsibility in its application. . . .' " The assistant director's face was radiant; his hands had begun to shake. It looked like we were in for something big. Bruns was dozing, and I saw now that he was not alone. Dainard, too, noted the nodding heads and his voice grew in volume. "I am living proof of the rewards granted the creative imagination by this Bureau! *Mine was the. . . .*" But they still dozed.

No longer able to control his powerful voice, William J. Dainard fairly shouted, his echoes reverberating down the sparkling walls of Justice. Every new agent was on the edge of his chair now, endocrines doing double-duty . . . and I'm sure every agent walking the honey-combed passages of the Justice building heard as the big words came tumbling from his lips. "Mine was . . . THE CHILD-MOLESTER'S COLORING BOOK!" His hands shook violently as he held up a sample copy.

There was a silent moment as he loosened his collar and then continued. "Bureau psychologists worked out the instructions. Of course, the children were directed to color the bad man's clothing in dark colors, to get across the idea that he was sinister; his eyes were to be colored red, to show he was *bestial*. The book was issued depicting the various dodges used by the classic child-molester, such as the offering of candy or a ride home from school or help in crossing the street. Well, gentlemen," he said confidently, "let it suffice to say that it caught on like wildfire . . . especially as it bore the signature of the Director, J. Edgar Hoover."

# *Boys and Girls*
## COLOR THE PICTURE AND MEMORIZE THE RULES

## FOR YOUR PROTECTION, REMEMBER TO:

- Turn down gifts from strangers
- Refuse rides offered by strangers
- Avoid dark and lonely streets
- Know your local policeman

*J. Edgar Hoover*
Director, Federal Bureau of Investigation

Dainard glanced at his watch. "Gentlemen, I see there are but a few more minutes remaining, so I'll cut it short. But I want to make sure you are aware that atheistic communism is, in our Director's words, 'The single greatest menace facing our great nation today.' The Communist youth movement stands behind a high percentage of our juvenile delinquency, which is the major cause of the breakdown of the American family system. As our Director has said in one of his recent speeches, 'By spreading its poison through young veins, gangrenous communism is attempting to render the future generation of Americans a quadruple amputee—a nation without freedom of speech, press, assembly or religion. The youth of this nation, armed with the scalpel of truth, can and must cut this disease from the body of America!'

"The Director will be stressing this more and more every day, and if you are smart you will learn all you can about the *Commies* and their widespread activities on college campuses and their tremendous influences upon juvenile delinquency. Mark my words, gentlemen, it will not be long before the Director publicly pin-points the Communist threat to our nation's youth as a far greater danger than a CPUSA takeover of our government."

The assistant director stepped down from the podium and slowly and theatrically walked down the aisles that separated our desks, looking each one of us in the eye as he passed.

"And you know," he concluded, "it's a damned good thing he's concentrating on it. Because you see—our Director and his Bureau are the only weapons the American people have with which to subdue this menace . . ." He paced slowly to the front of the class and stood staring up at the Stars and Stripes as he issued his final words:

*"Thank God for the F.B.I.!"*

After dinner that evening I walked out into the chill Washington winter and took a leisurely stroll over to the Library of Congress. Keady had handed out brochures on F.B.I. history earlier in the week, and on the last page was a supplementary reading list which he had assigned as homework. Bruns laughed when I reminded him about it, claiming, "That's kid stuff, Norm. Don't pay any attention to it." But I'd never been to the Library of Congress before and I decided to look up the reading list anyway.

For over an hour, though, I was diverted by a fascinating display of Abraham Lincoln's personal effects. I couldn't get over it—his hat and reading glasses . . . even letters he had written in his own hand—all of them right there, less than a few inches away. And I couldn't help thinking that if there had been an F.B.I. around in those days such a man as John Wilkes Booth would never have fulfilled his hateful destiny.

When I finally did get around to the business at hand, I was surprised to learn that of the five books recommended as outside reading, three were children's books. And I was informed by an extremely polite elderly woman at the reference desk that none had *ever* been published in any other form than children's editions. Which left the two other books on my list, *The F.B.I. Story* and *Masters of Deceit* . . . and I had already read them both.

I wandered back to the Lincoln exhibit, thinking that even in his apathy my roommate really wasn't so dumb after all.

# 7

Every Friday at NAC, just before class was dismissed, Keady stood nervous and fidgeting before us, and regular as clock-work he would deliver his weekend admonition. "Now make sure you stay out of trouble," he would say.

The preface was always the same. But the remainder of his speech varied, depending upon which of the Bureau rules struck him as most likely to be sinned against on that particular weekend. I never could understand how he figured these things out.

But one of his favorites was the Bureau rule against unapproved nightclubs. "Remember the Director's dislike for agents who go out on the town at night . . ." was a familiar phrase.

After quoting at length from one of the Director's speeches on that very rule he would remind us of the penalty most likely to befall its violators. "Remember those two agents in the last class who were seen in an unapproved nightclub . . . and who were *fired* by the Director the very next day!"

The Bureau rules were clear enough. There were so many of them though that every time he moved, a new agent found himself violating at least one of them. The anti-nightclub rule didn't bother me particularly, although it did keep me out of some of the more *swinging* places that Bruns had told me about. But most of them, like that hotel on Pennsylvania Avenue, looked like clip-joints anyway. No, it was in an entirely different area that I found myself in a sudden and direct confrontation with the Bureau rules.

It was during our first week of training that Keady pointed out the Bureau's great concern for the physical condition of its agents, and when we learned there was a gym right there in the Justice building basement Bruns and I agreed that a twice weekly handball session would be just the thing to keep us in shape. And one day during our lunch hour we went down to the gym to check out their handball facilities.

Sure enough, a makeshift court was available. But when we approached the agent in charge, Butch Mayor, he told us quite simply that it would be impossible for us to use the gym after working hours because it was reserved for "agents with more seniority." We explained we were in class all day, but Butch just shrugged, saying, "That's the Bureau rules." And that was that.

A few days later, though, we learned that Butch closed the doors down tight at six o'clock every night: The gym was reserved for no one.

Our only alternative, if we were to play handball at all, was the G Street YMCA—although I soon found there was a specific Bureau rule against it. Agents were forbidden inside at any time. But Bruns assured me it was just like the Roosevelt—that agents came and went at the G Street YMCA and nothing ever happened. And I couldn't help but agree, since I'd read several articles in the Law Enforcement Bulletin where the Director lauded specific organizations of American youth, such as the Boy Scouts, the CYO. and particularly the Young Men's Christian Association.

The moment Bruns and I walked in the door of the G Street YMCA, though, I saw the reason behind that Bureau rule. On a wooden bench near the entrance a burly fellow, wearing shoulder-length hair and a visage of an ape, sat demurely beside a doe-skinned lad of seventeen. They smiled openly as we entered.

In the gym I noticed another pair swishing across the floor in skin-tight levis, wearing tennis shoes to match. Bruns remarked they made a charming couple.

And indeed, the G Street YMCA was a homosexual hotbed. But, for that matter, so was my home town—and they had never bothered me there either. It was just something one eventually got used to and ignored. Apparently Bruns felt the same way because after that first night he never even mentioned it. So glad were we to get the exercise that we reserved a handball court there twice a week for the rest of the time we were at NAC. And we had no problems.*

Several months later though, just as NAC was about to graduate, Bruns learned through the well established grapevine of Bureau clerks that Mohammed had indeed visited the mountain of Butch Mayor's gym in the form of Attorney General Robert Kennedy. A young and active man, the attorney general was working late one evening and decided to take his daily workout in the F.B.I. gymnasium. The door, of course, was locked. Butch Mayor was out on the town. And Kennedy was enraged.

From that day forward the doors to the basement gym in the Justice building remained open until eleven. Bruns and

---

*Although indeed the G Street YMCA was the very site of the arrest of Walter Jenkins, aide to President Lyndon Johnson, in 1964 on a morals charge.

I laughed so hard at the image of Butch Mayor's face when he learned that the attorney general of the United States had been down beating on the door to his gymnasium, that we could hardly sleep the night we heard about it.

*   *   *

This was far from the only confrontation that the youthful attorney general was to have with the F.B.I. The pot really began to boil while NAC was still in Washington, shortly after Kennedy had been assigned the post. And it started with a phone call.

We new agents had been warned repeatedly by our administrator to watch what we said over the Justice building telephones. When we asked him why, Keady just smiled.

But as always Bruns knew the answer: the phones were tapped. He even got one up on our administrator by telling us to be especially careful making calls from the Washington field office, located in the old post office (known affectionately in Bureauese as "the OPO") right next door to Justice, because they, too, were tapped; and apparently Hoover delighted in listening in on these particular phones at the oddest hours.

The clerks knew it, NAC knew it—but Robert Kennedy did not know the phones were tapped. And one day the Director himself was reported to have overheard the brand new attorney general saying that ". . . J. Edgar Hoover was just too damned old to run the Federal Bureau of Investigation in the nineteen-sixties!" It was never revealed to whom the attorney general was speaking. But it was common knowledge, according to Justice building gossips, that upon the re-election of John F. Kennedy in 1964 the Director would be definitely out.

The phone call was just the beginning. One afternoon, shortly after the Kennedy wire-tap incident, and just as Sam, the Director's colored receptionist, stepped down the hall for coffee, Kennedy arrived unannounced and most unexpectedly. Finding the outer office unmanned, the attorney general walked right in—only to discover the Director of the Federal Bureau of Investigation fast asleep on the office couch, enjoying his afternoon nap.

Kennedy was the first attorney general in several decades to take the Justice Department hierarchy seriously.

The attorney general, of course, stood at the top; the F.B.I. Director was technically his subordinate. *Technically.* But even the most militant and aggressive attorneys general of previous administrations (including both Rogers and Brownell) had avoided giving the Director assignments that might involve a direct application of authority. Not Kennedy though. Not long after the surprise visit Hoover received an unexpected phone call requesting *him,* the Director of the F.B.I., to appear in the office of the attorney general. Kennedy wanted to see him.

In the past, the attorney general made *his* way to the Director's office whenever a meeting between the two became necessary. So when Kennedy's request came it was ignored. A second call was made with the same result. The third call was made by Kennedy himself, and he *ordered* the Director to report to the attorney general's office—*immediately!*

NAC was milling about in the hallway just down from the Director's office when our administrator got the news. Keady rushed out in a purple frenzy and shooed us back into the classroom. Frantically, he warned us that any instant the Director would be coming down the hallway; that disaster was certain to befall anyone found loitering.

As the class found their way inside the classroom Bruns and I peeked out the door for a last look. And indeed, at that very moment the Director rounded the bend in the hallway, marching toward a showdown with the brother of the President of the United States. There was no self-pity in that bulldog face; there only *might* have been a trace of resignation in the stoop of his shoulders. But the strength and nobility and courage in the man were overwhelming.

\* \* \*

Today I can honestly agree with the men who say you never truly know a man until you have worked for him; who say that a man may be kind to his wife and children and to his animals—but to his employees, *ruthless*. For this was true. Working for Hoover as a special agent of the F.B.I. I found him on many occasions to be inordinately cruel and both morally and intellectually dishonest. But his greatness is unmistakable. The history of America has been shaped by the Director.

> "A strictly negative attitude or the philosophy of just staying afloat—all too common today—will never meet the impact of the communist challenge."
>
> J. Edgar Hoover, *Masters of Deceit*

# 8

A light snow had just begun to fall on that dreary December afternoon when we boarded the bus for the F.B.I. Academy at Quantico. The sun was setting. Only the outline of the capital city was visible, suddenly lifeless against a somber sky. But inside the bus was warm and comfortable, and I was proud to be there, and the feeling somehow reminded me of the year I had made the UCLA gymnastics traveling squad for the Pacific Coast Conference Finals. Here of course the stakes were infinitely higher. My entire future was involved. But it was the same warm feeling.

I had been thinking a great deal of home, mainly I suppose because I'd never been through an eastern winter before, but also because I knew that even in December my old surfing buddies would still be basking on the beach, living each day as it came and for what it was worth, and riding that Malibu surf. It's hard for someone who has never done it to appreciate the universal mysticism of those long green swells and how easily they get into a young man's blood. But they do. And their kind of freedom is a wonderful thing, where their only thought, their only responsibility is the next wave.

But such was not for me. It was great, those years, lying brown as a nut in the Malibu sand and listening to the old-

timers as they spun their untiring yarns of the old days—
"when boards were made of iron and men were made of
steel," as one of the grizzled old surf-mariners used to say.
But beyond that next wave they had nothing to look forward to. Living in the past as they did, barely able to stay
afloat financially and socially, hardly compared to a career
with the F.B.I. Yes, I was proud to be inside that bus.

"Quantico is an important step for you, fellows." It was
Keady. Our adminstrator stood at the front of the bus, holding onto the overhead railing with one hand, his clipboard
with the other. It was dark and I could barely make out the
tall shadows of trees against the sky as we sped through the
lush Virginia countryside. "The background you've had at
NAC will hold you for awhile. . . ." Over the sound of the
engine he was barely audible, particularly from where Bruns
and I sat toward the rear of the bus. "Of course you'll have
your regular classes at Quantico, too, but you'll be learning
a lot more about field techniques—surveillance, finger-print-
ing, making plaster casts of tire-tracks and foot-prints . . .
And you'll be qualifying on the PPC, the practice pistol
course. In fact you will become intimate with all the weapons
used in the field—the submachinegun and the grenade-firing
gas gun and a type of shotgun which fires rifle-loads so powerful they can penetrate a wood frame house. And many others
that you'll find out about soon enough.

"But before we get there I want to give you an idea of
what to expect from SAC William Bone . . ."

At that moment New Agent Thomas Robinson dropped off
to sleep. His prematurely balding head bobbed against an
emaciated chest as the old Bureau bus pounded and rattled
over the pockmarked Virginia highway. Not a few of us had
been lulled into somnolence by the rhythmic pounding.

Keady noted this but chose to ignore it, directing his words to those of us who still appeared alert.

"Remember, it's always a good idea to check up on the SAC whenever you're assigned to a new field office; if you have the opportunity you should always write him a personal letter expressing how much you look forward to working under him. Which will prepare you for writing the Director to compliment him on solving a big case or to thank him for making a personal visit to your area, or on his birthday, or on May tenth. . . ."

Suddenly Keady could no longer stand the sea of nodding heads before him. "Robinson!" he bellowed. New Agent Thomas Robinson lurched awake, his bleary eyes trying desperately to focus on the furious administrator. "Robinson, I don't suppose I have to tell you what May tenth stands for. . . ."

"No, sir. . . ."

"Well?" Keady demanded.

Somebody in the back of the bus began humming the strains of *Happy Birthday*. Robinson's head was still fuzzy. "It's the Director's birthday," he blurted before he even thought.

"Ro-bin-son . . ." the administrator began, slowly enunciating each syllable.

"I mean it's the date he was appointed acting director," said Robinson saving himself in the nick of time. Wide awake now, he looked around angrily for the hummer.

But Keady was not put off so easily. "What year, Robinson? And who appointed him?"

"Nineteen-twenty-four, by Attorney General Stone," the new agent answered correctly.

Satisfied, Keady returned quickly to his cautionary lecture while he still held a captive audience. "Now SAC Bone is a stickler for the strict observance of Bureau rules. That means no card playing; no cokes above the first floor. But his favorites are those rules prohibiting stock-market speculation and marriage without prior authorization from the Director. Now I've never told you about the agent who was all set to get married and remembered that rule at the last minute. Well, when we checked out his fiancée it was revealed that she had a brother in the CPUSA! A card-carrying Communist. . . ."

The entire trip took about two hours. Keady continued his admonitions for the rest of the journey, but the bus made so much noise most of it was completely lost. He had already been over the same ground time and time again and as my mind drifted I paid more attention to the man than to his words.

Only the day before, Bruns had given me fresh insight into our administrator. He was by far the most cautious man I'd ever met, meticulous in his concern for the details of Bureau ritual. Now I understood why.

According to Bruns, after ten years in the field Keady had been promoted to night supervisor in charge of the auto theft desk in an obscure field office. Over the next two years he rose from Auto Theft to Bank Robbery, and thence to Interstate Transportation of Stolen Property. And after those two years of working fourteen to sixteen hours a day with no mistakes (or at least no conspicuous ones, and without initialing anyone else's) he made it to field supervisor.

One more year and he was heralded to Washington for "further administrative training." After which he was assigned to the Seat of Government for three years, during which he served as a tour guide (to improve his public speaking abilities) and as a field office inspector (which involved traveling around to the fifty-seven field offices, ferreting out the mistakes of his fellow special agents and reporting them to the Director). Finally, as administrator of NAC George Keady was in direct line for promotion to *ASAC* (Assistant Special Agent in Charge) of one of the field offices.

Small wonder he was cautious. More than fifteen years of hard work were at stake; the outcome rested precariously in the clumsy hands of twenty-two new agents. A dangerous situation. No civil service guaranteed his promotion. If one of his new agents got into trouble . . . if the Director or even someone remotely close to the Director frowned on his performance as administrator of NAC his entire career was out the window. It was as simple as that.

Before I knew it we were slowing for the main gate to the Quantico Marine Base where the F.B.I. Academy was located. Amid blaring floodlights the Marine guard stood rigid in his winter greens, the tiny steam-puffs of his breath giving the only clue he was alive.

We bumped to a halt. His gunbelt and gloves were immaculate white, his face ashen and expressionless. His grey eyes jumped to the F.B.I. sticker on the windshield. Uttering one crisp word, he snapped us a mechanical salute. "Proceed!" the voice said. And a moment later we pulled up in front of a large brick building which was to be our Quantico home.

Keady counted heads as we disembarked into the chill Virginia darkness, carrying our luggage, and when we had all assembled he explained the general layout of the Academy, concluding with a note about the eating facilities. "And for God's sake, fellows, don't complain about the food. If you do you're sure to get a personal letter of censure from the Director. Besides, *it's good family-style* food. . . ."

And on that note our training at the Quantico Academy began.

# 9

Our three-story brick building faced onto the busiest road on the entire base, about a mile from the main gate. As F.B.I. personnel we were privileged to sleep until seven-thirty every morning, much to the Marines' chagrin. Up with the sun every morning, they weren't about to let us forget it. And to get even, every platoon on the base went out of its way to march by the F.B.I. facility, counting cadence and yelling at the top of their lungs; no Marine vehicle failed to race its engine and grind its gears as it passed our dormitory windows at daybreak. But it was all in fun, the Marines were always friendly, and the rivalry only served to add spice to our training at Quantico.

The entire top floor was taken up by our five-man dorms; the second floor too. (Though there was one mysteriously locked and guarded room on the top floor that was to bring me dangerously close to the biggest trouble of my infant career.)

Bruns and I shared a dorm with none other than Thomas Robinson and two other characters who were really quite amusing. One of them, Davis Pennington, loved nothing in the world better than sleep, while we sat around after hours talking.

Pennington hit the sack right after dinner. And to keep the light from interfering with his pleasure he worked one of his heavy wool socks into a handy blindfold. Our fifth roommate, Adam Eustis, spent most of his off-hours in front of the television set in the lounge. And we never saw much of him until one day a large storm swept away the TV antenna and he suddenly appeared for our late evening bull-sessions two nights in a row. We were all glad when the antenna was replaced.

The ground floor was devoted to classrooms, the lounge where Eustis' television was located, and the dining hall. And squeezed into a small corner of the basement was our gymnasium. Unlike the basement gym in the Justice building, though, this one was well used, even though most of the floor-space was devoted to housing an impressive arsenal which made the place look something like a revolutionary's hideout. And as a matter of fact our defensive tactics instructor did look a little like Pancho Villa.

Swarthy and dark and incredibly ugly and deformed (from his years of professional football, Keady told us), this giant of a man stood six and a half feet tall, wearing the armor of nearly three hundred pounds of lean, charging muscle. Withstanding even the stormy seas of Bureau ritual, of SAC's ASAC's and special agents, of government forms and Standard Operating Procedures, he was known to everyone simply as *Big Z*. Strangely, more than any other single factor, it was the incongruous good nature of the big man that brought me through Quantico unscathed.

The training itself was not all that rigorous. Just as in Washington the written exams were easy: we were given the answers well in advance. And, too, the physical training was not all it had been cracked up to be. It seemed geared for men like Robinson who, if their lives depended upon it, could squeeze out ten passable push-ups, but no more. If this was the kind of training given our World War II Commandos, I thought, no wonder so few of them came back alive. But I passed it off when someone suggested we were lucky to be there in winter when the weather prevented our instructors from running us through the Virginia countryside for hours, as Keady had promised. Even the Marines, it was said, had a soft time during the winter.

No, the training was easy. Whether you made it or not hinged on your ability to stay awake in class. And in Big Z's classes, not an eyelash flickered.

The first glimpse of the man was terrifying. I walked into the basement gym for our first class meeting, and the smell hit me like a sledge-hammer, a rare blend of rancid sweat-sox and the heavy grease called *Cosmoline* which prevented the Quantico arsenal from rusting away in the subterranean dampness. But suddenly—there he was in the corner, by the blackboard, dressed in a grey sweat-suit just as we were. Only where ours were loose and floppy his stretched skin-tight over his brawny back and shoulders, the pants-legs straining at his beefy calves. Dark and ominous as a panther he watched, motionless until the entire class had assembled.

He moved forward. "Don't just stand there like rocks," he growled. "Move right on in here. Close up where we can get a good look at each other." The voice boomed thick and powerful, like the man. "Just set yourselves down there on the mat," he said gesturing with an arm as big around as my thigh. Big Z waited until we were settled on the thick padded floor that reminded me of my gymnastics days in college. And then, reading our names from the roster he ordered us to stand, appraising each new agent as he did. I had the feeling we were about to be put up for sale.

"Well, you're not a very pretty lot," he said hopelessly when he'd finished. "But I guess you'll have to do. And to get you in shape we'll be having a night firing exercise later in the week. *In the snow!* Because, like the Director tells us, 'Crime knows no time, no clime, but confronts us every minute of the day!' "

So went our first meeting with the defense tactics instructor. And for the rest of our days at Quantico, whenever we had one of Big Z's classes, his lecture inevitably began with a quote from the Director; and he always concluded with a quote from the newspaper about a recent F.B.I. victory.

One memorable afternoon Big Z opened up with a quote about physical fitness. And as he spoke the giant roamed among us, peering down at each new agent as he passed—until finally he came to Robinson. For an instant it looked like Big Z was going to choke him, but he only grabbed the startled fellow by the scruff of the neck and hauled him up in front of the class, quoting from the Director all the while. "Robinson," he growled, "I'm gonna use you as the classroom dummy."

The new agent said nothing. I thought he was an admirable choice.

"Today we're gonna talk about certain delicate and vulnerable areas of the body. . . ." His whole face grinned, then he made a fist and threatened to demolish poor Robinson's groin with a savage uppercut. Robinson tried not to move. He was doing his best to be a good mannequin. He looked away nervously. "Now when I mention those *delicate* areas I'm talking about *defensive* tactics," said Big Z. "*Offensive* tactics in that area you gotta work out on your own." Everybody laughed but Robinson.

By this time we'd gotten used to the idea that beneath the rough exterior Big Z was quite another man. In fact after we had recovered from that fearsome first impression we were quite at ease with him. He was more like a regular guy than any of the instructors we'd had in Washington. And he was a natural ham besides. His voice was strangely flexible and he changed it to suit the occasion; and he could screw his huge plastic face into a thousand hilarious expressions. Down in that basement the atmosphere was almost vaudevillian. And each class was a masterful performance.

Now Big Z handed his reluctant assistant a blackjack. Robinson examined it suspiciously for a few moments as if it were a live hand-grenade. Then, feigning self-confidence, he gave the thong several turns around his wrist and gripped it tightly in preparation for his role.

"Now when you want to break a hold," Big Z explained seriously, "you gotta choose a part of the body that's got nerves and pain centers up close to the skin. No matter how hard you hit a guy where he's got heavy muscles for protection it won't take effect right off. It's like playin' football. You guys all played ball didn't ya?" He looked at us expectantly. Only a few heads nodded. "Well, those of you that did will remember doin' real good out there on the field, and even though you got knocked around a lot it didn't bother you none. At least not right off. You'd go out with your girl that night—and you'd do real good there, too . . ."

He grinned, and the class exploded with laughter as he danced toward Robinson, whose head barely reached his chest. He placed a huge paw on the new agent's shoulder and continued. "Well, those body-blows never bothered you at all until the next day. *Then* you couldn't move so well. But that's too late when you're trying to get a guy offa your back. You want to give that guy instant *pain!* And to do that you gotta concentrate on the shins, knuckles, groin, and the bridge of his nose. . . ." He stepped away from Robinson slowly, then squared off to face him. The new agent paled visibly, clutching the blackjack ever tighter. The veins in his puny forearm stuck out like vines. "Now watch me," Big Z growled, stalking him like a huge cat.

Thomas Robinson did his best. But in an instant Big Z was swarming all over the poor fellow, and in disarming him of the blackjack it looked like he nearly broke his arm.

The instructor threw his hands in despair. "Okay, okay," he muttered. Clutching his arm, Robinson made a move toward his place on the mat. Big Z stopped him. "Wait a minute, Robinson, I'm not through with you yet. Here . . ." He handed him the blackjack and looped the thong over the new agent's thumb for him. "Don't ever wrap it around the wrist; loop it over the thumb or the index finger, bring it around the back of the hand, and *then* grab ahold of the butt. That way it's secure enough, but you can also let go quick enough if you have to.

"And you use it like a hammer—short, snappy blows using the wrist and forearm are best. Round-house blows with the whole arm like you just tried are too slow and inaccurate. . . ." He pulled the weapon away from Robinson. "You can also turn the blackjack around and grab the heavy end of it and jab with the tip of it like this." He jerked it toward the new agent's pot belly.

"Now instinct tells you to go straight for your enemy's head, but that's the easiest thing for him to defend, and the movement leaves you open to counter-attack. It's hard to control the force of head-blows, too . . . and how are you ever going to know how thick a guy's skull is? Remember, you don't always want to kill him, you just want to put him out of business. If you *have* to hit him in the head, though, aim for the point of the chin or the side of the neck. Otherwise, the best areas to aim for are the joints—the wrist, elbow, shoulder, knee, and ankles—or other vulnerable spots like the collar-bone, forearm, upper arm, thigh, kidneys, or the pit of the stomach."

Big Z turned back to Robinson. "Now a good way to do it is to fake toward the head and then hit him in the knee or some other place away from the head. Come here, Robinson, and we'll show 'em how to do it." Robinson gave a loud sigh and prepared to again disgrace us.

Toward the end of the day Big Z excused Robinson, who by this time could hardly stand. Then he proceeded to unfold the entire front page of an Alexandria, Virginia, newspaper, walking down among us as he did, so we would all be sure to catch the headline. "F.B.I. CAPTURES TOP TEN FUGITIVE," it read. He walked slowly to the front of the class, then paused for a long moment. It was too early for the lecture to be over. Big Z was up to something, I reasoned. Carefully, he re-folded the paper and replaced it on the table. He picked up the blackjack Robinson had abandoned there, slapping it against the palm of his hand, giving emphasis to his words. "The F.B.I. *The Federal Bureau of Investigation*," he enunciated slowly. "You!"

And now as he spoke his voice began to rise, growing louder as it did. "Every one of you guys has been through at least four years of college, and most of you have studied law or accounting besides, and pretty soon your thirteen weeks of F.B.I. training is gonna be up . . . and the Director's gonna send you out to bring in some four hundred pound stevedore!" Now the giant fairly roared. "And what are you going to do?" He slammed the blackjack back down on the table. "I repeat: WHAT ARE YOU GOING TO DO?"

Snarling and muttering under his breath, his tiny pig's eyes filled with fire, the defensive tactics instructor lumbered through the class, stopping before each new agent in his path as he repeated the same question. When he came to Robinson I figured the poor fellow would faint dead away, but Big Z stalked on past him, stopping instead before Bruns, who was next to me.

Big Z looked like a volcano that was about to erupt. He hesitated for one eternal instant, appraising the cool ex-F.B.I. clerk's expressionless face. I couldn't believe it. Bruns wasn't afraid. I was terrified. Big Z must have sensed it because in the next instant his eyes fell like molten fire, on me.

"What are you going to do, Ollestad?" he snarled.

I was speechless. What *was* I going to do?

He repeated the question, only louder this time, grabbing me by the shoulders as he did, pulling me slowly and effortlessly to my feet. I felt my knees begin to shake. An insane smile tugged at the steel trap that was the giant's mouth. My stomach sank. Whatever I did, I knew it had to be better than Robinson. I just had to. . . .

There was no time to think. Suddenly I was up there in front of the class; Big Z was crouched only a few yards away, ready to attack. "Okay, Ollestad, you are the F.B.I. *Now let's see you take me in!*" The smile eroded to a savage sneer. A pair of handcuffs and an old practice .38 thudded to the padded floor beneath my feet. The gym was dead quiet. I stared down at the weapons. "Come on, G-man," he mimicked, "let's see you take me in!"

The next few seconds were an eternity. I could hear the big man's breath coming long and heavy. Then from the front of the class, only a few feet away, there came a low laugh—so low nobody heard it but me. *Robinson!* Out of the corner of my eye I saw him, leaning forward, his mouth agape in a crazy leer as he prayed for my impending doom. "Go get 'em, Malibu," he whispered.

The son-of-a-bitch, I thought. I scooped up the handcuffs and the pistol and jumped back before the giant had a chance to react. "F.B.I., you're under arrest!" I shouted, but my voice sounded funny.

"Haw, haw, haw!" laughed Big Z.

My heart was pounding in my throat. "All right, you . . . ah, get over by that wall! Go on, move! Put your hands up, your palms flat against the wall . . . spread your legs. . . ."

Big Z didn't budge. He stood leering, leaning up against the wall, picking his teeth with one fingernail. His craggy features wore a bemused expression. I opened the handcuffs, then stuffed them inside my sweat-pants so they hung from the waist-band. I edged closer to Big Z, stopping about two feet from him. "Hands up!" I ordered again, jamming the .38 hard into his gut.

For a moment everything was fine. His hands rose slowly . . . until they reached his waist. Then all hell broke loose. That was the last thing I knew, for suddenly the gun was gone from my hand and I was jammed up tight against the wall and I heard myself groan as the giant wrenched my arm into a hammerlock. He held it for a few seconds, and then suddenly let go, turning his back on me, walking slowly toward the front of the class. I rubbed my shoulder. The arm hung limp, I thought it was broken. Big Z wasn't through yet. He whirled to face me again. Now there was a *knife* in his hand!

He circled to my right. "Know what to call a nigger with a razor, Ollestad?" he rasped.

"N-no," I stammered, my eyes riveted to that knife. I couldn't tell if it was real or not. I was scared anyway.

He was stalking me now. I moved to my left, closer to the class, until suddenly I felt the table behind me. He had me cornered!

"Well, Ollestad, you call that nigger . . . *sir!*"

The class laughed uproariously, insanely, and Big Z relaxed, dropped the knife to his side. He wasn't coming after me, but I felt like an ass. As I reached back to steady myself against the table my hand brushed against the *blackjack,* and at that same instant I heard Robinson's high-pitched laugh above all the others, and I went mad. Big Z still stood there, his huge ape's arms dangling loose at his side, reveling in their adulation. And his words came pounding through my head—*"A short chopping blow . . . like striking a nail with a hammer!"*

My heart was racing as he turned toward me with that knife, and before I even realized what was happening I came down with the blackjack, hammering it savagely into the side of his neck, and I heard the crack as his head snapped and he crashed down like a wounded buffalo to the matting.

I'd have sworn he was dead. The class stared, incredulous at what had happened, the laughter frozen on their faces. After a stunned moment, Big Z shook his head, then jerked to his feet and as his eyes focused he started for me again. Just in time he checked himself; one more step and he would have decked me. Slowly his arms fell back to his sides as he collected his senses and tried to fully understand just what had happened. "What . . . why did you do it, Ollestad?" he whispered. *"Why on earth did you ever do it?"*

I couldn't answer. My mouth refused to form the words, and besides there were none. Maybe it was Robinson . . . maybe I was tired of him disgracing our class. And maybe it was the feeling of pride that comes with being an F.B.I.

agent . . . and Big Z had challenged that pride. Whatever it was, it was stupid. Big Z could have killed me in an instant.

He watched me for a few moments more, then bent to pick up the knife, lying at his feet, his eyes searching mine as he did. I could have sworn he smiled as he carefully and deliberately bent the knife in two and stuffed it inside his pocket. A rubber knife.

He motioned for me to sit down. As I brushed past Robinson he gave me a dirty look and mumbled something I couldn't hear. I ignored him. Big Z didn't. "At least Ollestad has balls," he said. That was all. Robinson flushed. He got the message.

Now the big man began pacing back and forth in front of the blackboard. "You started out all right, Ollestad," he began, "but you made several bad mistakes. Any one of them might have cost you your life. First of all, never point your revolver at anyone unless you intend to kill him. If the suspect is unarmed, there's no reason to draw it in the first place. On the other hand, if he is armed and you do draw it, never—never get within arm's length of that man! A .38 slug will travel a lot farther than the length of his arm. But get that pistol close enough and he's liable to take it away and jam it up your ass!

"Another thing. Take the easy way out when you're making an arrest: always bring several other agents along with you. If a guy sees he's outnumbered he's not liable to try to escape. If he's a big man and you are alone, don't be in a hurry. What's the rush? Wait him out." Big Z turned back to me. "In this case, Ollestad, you should have taken your own sweet time . . . and you really should have noticed the bulge in my pocket which indicated I was carrying a weapon. If it ever happens again—and believe me, it probably will—

keep your distance until the guy gets into a position where he can be searched safely. If he doesn't, radio for help.

"Now the position you tried to get me into—up against that wall—is pretty safe. The suspect is off balance and can't move until he recovers his balance, which gives you plenty of time to act. Another thing—notice that if anyone jams a gun in your ribs you can always shove it away before he has time to pull the trigger. You've got the element of surprise in your favor; you *know* when you're going to move and he doesn't and his reaction time isn't fast enough to compensate.

"All right, pair off and let's run through it together. Ollestad, you take Robinson. . . ."

In just such a manner Big Z was able to prepare us in self-defense. And we enjoyed every minute of it.

# 10

NAC learned a lot from Big Z and from the tobacco-chewing firearms instructors as well. Quite in contrast to their brethren back at the Seat of Government, they were an affable and gregarious lot, and because of them our training at the Quantico Academy passed smoothly and quickly. But our head instructor was a man of a different mold, as nervous and melancholy as our administrator was cautious. NAC had heard the stories about this man named Elmer Farmer, and we avoided him like the plague. We didn't have too much contact with him, but when he did appear it was when he was least expected.

Every day, though, right after lunch when everyone was drowsy was his one regular and favorite time; we could always depend upon him to come peeking in on the class to make sure everyone was awake. And whenever he did catch someone dozing he puffed up his lips like a Ubangi, and with his kinky hair and the way he craned his neck inside the doorway, we called him "Gladstone Gander."

And of course the day finally arrived when it was the head instructor's turn to conduct the weekly interview of the new agents' class.

Somehow I received the dubious honor of going first. And right after lunch I walked boldly into his office, trying my best to affect an air of confidence. He didn't even notice me at first, standing there by the window as he was, going over some papers with another instructor. As I stood there deliberating whether I should go back out and knock or simply announce myself I enjoyed my first close look at the head instructor.

The first thing I noticed was that he had the worst case of dandruff I'd ever seen. His skin, too, was flaky and dry. I figured it was on account of nerves. Then I noticed the clothes. He and Keady must have gone to the same tailor, I thought. Elmer Farmer wore the same expensive but ill-fitting blue serge suit that flopped down around his ankles like bell-bottoms. He'd have been right in style thirty years ago, chasing Dillinger around in a Stutz Bearcat, but I thought he looked more than slightly ridiculous here in the nineteen-sixties.

"Wh-what can I d-do for you?" came his sudden voice. I had been noticed. The head instructor stood squinting at me over his steel-rimmed reading glasses. And he did stutter just like Bruns had told me. And, too, he must have read my mind as I stood staring at his clothes, for when I told him my name and that I was from NAC he looked me over carefully from head to toe. "Those b-button down collars are going to get you in a p-peck of trouble," he stammered. But that was all, and I was relieved.

I was motioned to a seat across from the head instructor's desk; he dismissed the other instructor, and then spent a full two minutes rummaging through his desk drawer, finally extracting a dog-eared interview check-list.

"Th-this'll be your ten-week interview, Ottesen," he stammered nervously.

"*Ollestad,* sir," I corrected him. I was about to mention we were only in our seventh week of training, but I thought better of it. And I'd thought *I* was the one who was supposed to be nervous.

"Yes, yes—*Ollestad*. There are so many of you S-swedes running around . . . but that's what the Bureau is, a melting pot. Just like our grand country. Now where was I? Oh yes, the first question. . . ." His nervous eyes jumped back to the check-list, then fled to another mimeographed sheet. "I see you've got all B's in your classes, Ollestad. Now that's okay, but remember any new agent who drops below a B will be fired automatically!" He shot me a hard look, then fled back to the check-list. From past interviews I knew what was coming next. I braced myself for the most important question.

The head instructor leaned back in his chair and tried to look casual. "Do you have any problems, Ottesen?"

I looked serious. And I forgot about correcting him again. "No sir," I replied. That was the expected answer. But they always ignored it.

"Now we are m-more than w-willing to help new agents in any way we can. As our Director has said on many occasions, 'Nothing gives me more pride than to have a new agent come to me personally for counsel and advice. . . .'" He paused and re-phrased the original question. "Are you *sure* there's nothing you want to talk about?"

I thought for a moment. Which was a mistake. "No, sir," I answered.

"Are you absolutely sure, Ottesen? It's very important to us that you air your p-problems. We do have a r-right to know about them, you know. . . ." That moment's hesitation had made him suspicious that I was hiding something. And for the next ten minutes he did his best to find out what it was. I relaxed when he finally took a deep breath and returned to the questionnaire—a sure sign the *real* interview was over. He plodded through the rest of the questions hardly listening to my answers.

"How do you like the f-food here at the Academy?"

"Fine, sir."

"H-how do you like the service at meal times?"

"Fine."

"How are your instructors—any complaints?"

"No, sir."

"And how is your administrator, Mister. . . ." He searched his memory.

"Uh, your administrator—h-how is he treating you?"

"Fine."

"Good," he said setting the check-list aside. "Now, Mister Ottesen, your class will be meeting the Director p-*personally* in a few weeks, back at the seat of government, and I want you to remember to speak out loudly and d-distinctly when you are asked questions . . ."

"Yes, sir."

"Louder, Ottesen. L-look, the Director d-doesn't like s-sissies. You'll have to l-learn to s-speak up!" I said nothing, which only served to fuel his ardor.

"We're t-trying very hard to g-get you in s-some sort of shape to m-meet the Director. And you're not even t-trying. . . ." He stared over his glasses. I glanced out the window. The more excited he got the more he stuttered. "N-now I have a m-*motto* that I use when I meet with the Director— '*Sometimes wrong but never in doubt.*' Know what I mean, Ottesen? Everything you say and do must be *positive*. If you look away from the Director's face like you just did with me you'll be fired! Just like that. If there's a quiver in your voice or you wipe your mouth or pick at your nose . . . well, Ottesen, the Director doesn't miss things like that. They're signs of *weakness!* Another thing—don't ever let me catch you standing around in the corridors with your hands in your pockets. D-deviates do that. Playing with themselves. You know . . . *p-pocket p-pool.* . . ."

With that, Elmer Farmer's lemonish face puckered up into a wry smile, and he laughed much more heartily than I would have ever thought him able. Never before had I heard anyone stutter and laugh at the same time. And the effect was so funny I laughed right along with him. He seemed pleased. And still chuckling, he informed me that the interview was concluded, that I was excused.

As I turned to leave, he made one parting comment. "Re-remember, Ottesen, as our Director tells us, 'All of us have got to strive for g-goals that are higher and nobler. A negative attitude or philosophy of j-just staying afloat will not m-meet the challenge of this t-training school."

A few days later, right after lunch, and just as Keady was concluding one of his dreary war-stories, the door opened and in walked the head instructor. We figured it was just part of his daily wake-up routine, but no. Apparently Keady had been expecting him. With no explanation he nodded to our visitor and then took a seat toward the rear of the class. Elmer Farmer walked briskly to the podium and deposited a sheaf of papers.

"You will all be glad to know that I have completed your personal interviews and everything is fine. Just fine." He mustered a smile for Keady's benefit. His reading glasses kept slipping down over his nose as he spoke. "And today I would like to finish up with a few general questions." And he glanced at the seating chart.

"Larry Gilligan. . . ." He paused and looked around the room over his glasses.

New Agent Larry Gilligan was the most nervous fellow in

our class, and at the sound of his name he shot up, almost by reflex. His knee banged his desk on the way up, which only compounded the new agent's nervousness. He wilted visibly as his eyes met those of the head instructor.

"Mister Gilligan, what is the rule regarding agents engaging in financial speculation?"

Gilligan organized his thoughts and opened his mouth, prepared to answer and then gulped it shut as he remembered he was chewing *gum!* He swallowed, and tried to cover his mouth with his hand, but not in time.

"Mister Gilligan—do I see you chewing gum?"

Elmer Farmer removed the glasses from his nose, staring all the while at the hapless Gilligan. He repeated the question, incredulous that such a flagrant violation of the Academy rules had occurred before his very eyes.

"N-no, sir," Gilligan choked.

The two stared, their eyes locked. In front of the class he was fine; apparently it was only individual confrontations that shook him up.

"What was that in your mouth then, Gilligan?" said Farmer after a long pause. Now his tone was almost gentle, almost as if he were giving the new agent a chance when his guilt was obvious to everyone.

"J-just a hair. And I b-brushed it away. That was all, sir."

"Are you sure?"

"Yes, sir."

It was clear that New Agent Larry Gilligan was going to stick to his story. And Farmer thought that was just fine. Now there would be no reports to the Seat of Government, no letters of explanation to the Director. Indeed, the head instructor of the Quantico Academy was pleased, and he showed it. If there was one thing he admired it was a man who had learned to avoid trouble.

# 11

The firing range where our firearms classes were held was separated from the Academy by ten miles of heavily wooded rolling countryside, and even considering the old Bureau bus which ferried us to and from the range, our early morning trips through that birch-tree wilderness were beautiful. In that forest was a peacefulness. Gazing out at frozen meadows and stark black trees was one of the few times during training that I could relax completely. Somehow, the quiet of it all reminded me of Malibu's winter ocean and those soundless days in December and January when the sea stretched out almost too flat and glassy, just before the big storms hit.

But Keady just couldn't leave it alone. "That's Mount Vernon landscape . . . just like in George Washington's day," he always announced about halfway to the range. Then he'd mumble a few spontaneous remarks about the history of Valley Forge (Bruns told me he'd memorized them as a Justice Building tour guide), which always somehow reminded him of "a few choice words on the subject (which was now patriotism) from our Director." The words varied, but their spirit was always the same. And I for one was always glad to get to the range.

But one glorious Monday when the sky was incredibly

blue and the hillside had been swept blinding white by last night's snowfall, our administrator sat strangely silent. No Valley Forge, no quote from the Director—in fact he said nothing during the entire trip. Perhaps, I thought, he was overwhelmed by the beauty of it all. But as we dismounted and stood around shifting from one foot to the other, rubbing our hands together in a vain attempt to keep warm, and I saw the tightness around his mouth as he waited for us to assemble, I knew something was up. It was not long in coming.

"Fellows, I have something to say to you this morning. And I will say it only once. Afterwards there will be no questions. Have I made myself quite clear?" His keen eyes searched from one bewildered face to another to make sure we understood the import of his words. I wondered what it could be. It had to be something serious. The only other time I'd seen him so desperate was when the Director was on his way to the attorney general's office back in Washington, and Keady had been afraid NAC would be caught loitering in the corridor during our break.

"An order has been issued by SAC, Quantico," said Keady. His voice sounded mechanical and hollow. "It states that henceforth no F.B.I. personnel shall use the Coke machine located at the southwest corner of the Quantico rifle range. And, fellows," he added cautiously, "I'm sure I don't have to tell you what violation of this order would mean . . . *to all of us!*"

With that our administrator turned on his heel and nodded to one of our firearms instructors, who took over the class for the rest of the day. I was mystified and said as much to Bruns, who just shrugged and said simply, "The man said no Cokes, so no Cokes it is." That was that. And for the rest of the day we were so busy on the range we should have been able to forget about it.

The "range," as it was called, was actually a complex of several different ranges, each designed to accommodate a specific weapon. There were the rifle ranges and the practice pistol course and various other courses set aside for the gas gun, sub-machine-gun and shotgun; and there were even facilities for dueling and skeet-shooting. And there in the southwest corner of the rifle range stood the Coke machine, heretofore innocent and inconspicuous, virtually unattended in the dead of winter.

But the day of Keady's admonition it enjoyed a sudden flurry of clandestine interest: We all developed tremendous thirsts for coke. And every time NAC came marching by, the little red machine nearly drove us nuts.

But it was only momentary, and by noon the next day the coke machine was again forgotten—until Bruns and I overheard the firearms instructors joking about it over lunch in the firing range cafeteria. After Keady's no-questions edict I wasn't about to stick my neck out by asking what the mystery was all about, and I resigned myself to trying to pick up what I could from the conversation. Finally, I was able to piece it together. Incredible as it seemed, the Coke machine had been *robbed*. Someone had made off with the grand sum of four dollars and forty cents in change and thirty-two ice cold Cokes.

I looked at Bruns, but he gave no sign he had even heard. And before I had a chance to say anything we were back on the range, working like dogs for the rest of the afternoon. Bruns slept all the way to the Academy and after we got to the dorm Robinson hung around all evening. The way he'd been running to Keady with class gossip I was afraid to talk about anything in front of him.

Robinson was constantly scribbling in that tiny notebook of his. If we complained about the weather I was sure Keady would eventually get wind of it. But our stool-pigeon finally took off with Eustis for the lounge and we had our chance. I was bursting to hear what Bruns had to say about it. I figured he was as excited about the Coke machine mystery as I was.

The night was colder than usual, and Bruns was piling another blanket on his bed. I sat down on my bed next to his. "Can you beat that, Bill? Somebody actually robbed the F.B.I. and got away with it. . . ."

"How about that?" he yawned. "I don't mean to sound disinterested, Norm, but it's not the first time that's happened and it probably won't be the last."

"Why . . . what do you mean? Don't you even care . . . ?"

"Sure I care. But what are you going to do about it?"

"Well, we sure ought to do *something*. I don't care what Keady said, we ought to try to catch whoever did it. It makes us look bad, getting robbed and then standing around and not doing anything about it. From what I hear, SAC Bone is a pretty tough bird. I'll bet he's working on it right now. . . ."

Bruns climbed into bed and sighed loudly. "You'll have to talk to Big Z, he's SAC for the time being."

"Are you nuts?"

"No, Norm, I'm not." He sounded bored. His unconcerned attitude was beginning to irritate me. Bruns saw that and explained. "Bone checked out on leave the same day Keady told us about the Coke machine thing . . . I was in the office Monday evening when he left . . ."

"But Bone is still responsible for the robbery," I interrupted. "He was on duty when it happened."

"No, I saw the log, Norm, and Bone worked it so his leave appeared to have started Saturday, the day before it happened."

"But that means Big Z will get hung for it!" I was really mad now. "That's all the more reason to catch the guy who did it. Bone should have faced up to it and launched a full-scale investigation!"

"Forget it, Ollestad. I could go the rest of my life without a Coke."

"Bruns—that's not the point at all and you know it!"

"Sure it is," he answered calmly. "There's not going to be any trouble unless somebody makes waves. Now you're your own boss and you can do any damned fool thing you want to. Just leave me out of it, that's all I ask. Okay?" He rolled over before I could answer and a moment later he was snoring.

I was too stirred up to sleep much that night. The next day I decided to scout around a little to see what I could dig up on my own. But Bruns' warning still rang in my ears and I resolved not to say anything to anyone.

That evening I uncovered my first clue. I'd signed out for the movie over at the Marine PX, but it was a terrible film and I left early. On my way back I stopped by the coffee shop. The place was practically empty. A pair of hilariously drunk Marines hung over their coffee trying to focus their bleary eyes on the clock over the counter; they were arguing over the time. And of course the problem was they couldn't tell which hand on the clock was which. One of the fellows was convinced it was ten o'clock (which it was), while the other was ready to bet his stripes (he had only one) it was ten till twelve.

Of all things, I ordered a coke, my first in more than ten years. After a few minutes of polite conversation with the soda-jerk, I worked around to the subject of Coke machines, mentioning that I'd heard somebody on the base was doing a pretty good business emptying the coin boxes and taking the bottles as well. His reply stopped me cold. All soft drinks were ordered through the PX, and although there were many different kinds of machines on the base, the only one that dispensed bottles was the one on the range. I was elated. All I'd have to do was track down the bottles. I was confident the thief stole the Cokes for his own thirst; there wouldn't have been much of a market for them in town. Sooner or later I'd find those bottles. And they would lead me to my man.

On the way back to the Academy I checked every trash can in sight. Most had been emptied recently, and all I came up with were two bottles of cheap bourbon.

Thursday found us back on the range again, the rifle range this time, the site of the robbery. We were late getting started, and when I glanced toward the machine I saw the reason. Our instructor was huddled over the machine with a man in a white workman's outfit. Keady was nowhere in sight, so I moved closer to see if I could pick up some clues.

At first I could only make out that they were joking about the robbery, but as I edged up behind them I heard the workman, who was apparently the service man from the PX, telling the instructor that even he had no idea how the robbery had occurred, unless of course the thief had a key.

"Look for yourself," he said, "there's not a mark on her. It's a sure thing he didn't jimmy it. The only thing I can't figure out is the water in the coin box . . . ."

Suddenly I was noticed. "What are you doing sneaking up on us, Ollestad?" growled the instructor.

"I . . ."

"Didn't your administrator give you the word about the SAC's order against using the Coke machine?"

"Yes, sir . . . I . . . only wanted to borrow your combination tool. The bolt in my rifle's jammed." I don't know where I got the excuse, but it worked. And a few minutes later we were out on the firing range.

Friday too we were on the range. And that evening after the bus pulled up in back of the Academy I dismounted and just happened to glance at the trash barrels that stood by the kitchen door. I stopped dead in my tracks. The barrels were full, and lying right on top of the piled-up trash were the empty Coke bottles. Three of them! The thief was right there in the Academy.

I spent the entire weekend reading for a required book report by a window on the second floor, overlooking the trash barrels. The crime had occurred late last Sunday, from what I had overheard of the firearms instructor's conversation, and I reasoned that even if the thief drank four Cokes a day he'd still have a few bottles left. And sure enough, at precisely three forty-five that afternoon, exactly one week after the robbery, the kitchen door opened and one of the Negro waiters walked boldly over to the trash barrel and deposited a hot Coke bottle on the heap. I had found my man.

That night at dinner I was so busy watching for the fellow I hardly touched my food—until I caught Robinson eyeing me suspiciously, and then I wolfed down the whole meal in less than a minute. But suddenly, amid a clattering of plates and silverware, there he was—my man, wheeling his bus-boy's dolly up and down the aisles, his eyes darting from one table to the next as he collected the dirty tableware, completely oblivious to my discovery of his crime. He moved to our table and began clearing away the dishes. I could hear my heart thumping. I glanced at his badge, then looked away quickly so as not to be caught staring. Two-thirteen it read. I'd never forget that number.

I had him, that much I was sure. But how to prove it was my next problem. And I decided the best way would be to photograph him in the act of disposing of the evidence. So since the trash area was well lighted with floodlights, I returned that very night to my second story window with my box camera. It wasn't ideal but it took good clear pictures and the window wasn't very far from the trash heap.

About seven-thirty I began to tire of the whole thing. I hadn't had much sleep the night before, and we had a rough day ahead of us, and just as I was ready to call it quits for the night, the kitchen door opened and out into the floodlights walked two-thirteen. All he had to do was dump the bottles and he was mine. I was all set with the camera. Then I got a sudden sick feeling in my stomach as I squinted through the view-finder and saw that there were no bottles, that indeed his arms were empty but for a tiny paper package too small to contain Coke bottles. I watched as two-thirteen mounted a bicycle and peddled off into the darkness.

I must have stood by the window for a full minute before it dawned on me that he hadn't gone toward town, as he should have, he was headed for the range!

I rushed downstairs, practically colliding with Robinson on the first floor landing, and in my excitement I almost forgot to sign out. It was a good thing I did because as I left the office Robinson was loitering outside the door. It was obvious he was waiting for me.

"Where are you going, Ollestad?" he asked suspiciously.

"Can't talk," I yelled. "Going to be late for the movie . . .

it's *The F.B.I. Story*," I added, remembering that was what was playing at the base theatre. I rushed around the back of the Academy building where I'd seen another bicycle parked up against the wall, hoping Robinson wouldn't try to follow and botch up the whole thing. I peddled off like crazy toward the range.

The night was ink black and the bike tires kept slipping on the icy road. I figured I was no more than three or four minutes behind him, and since he was probably in no hurry and since it was ten miles to the range I'd have no trouble catching up to him. The air was freezing but in a few minutes the sweat was streaming down my face. I felt icy. And I could feel the cold air all the way down in my lungs.

Sure enough, even before the tall trees guarding the range entrance jutted into view I could hear the rhythmic clank of the bike chain up ahead as he peddled closer and closer to the little red Coke machine and his undoing.

Suddenly we were there. I watched his dark form glide slowly through the entrance . . . but then as he was swallowed up by darkness the clanking stopped. Had he spotted me? I braked to a stop, listening. I could hear only the wind in the trees as it came sweeping across the frozen wilderness. I waited a full minute, and still no sound. Almost as if by command the moon slid from behind the clouds and I could make out the road as it stretched out toward the rifle range, then sloped down for the final approach to the parking area. Then it came to me. What a fool I was! My man was coasting; that explained the silence. By now he must already be there by the machine. I had to hurry!

Peddling as fast as I could for the downhill run, I came over the rise like the very wind itself. My ears were frozen and I couldn't even feel my nose. I pulled up by the ammunition shack and set the bike down quietly. My feet made soft crunching sounds in the frozen earth as I crept toward the machine. I rounded the corner of the building and stopped dead as I heard the metallic sound of the Coke machine even before I saw him there kneeling beside the machine in the moonlight, less than ten yards away. I was close enough to see the beads of sweat glistening on his ebony skin and I could hear his heavy breathing. He worked slowly and methodically, as if he had all the time in the world. I watched as again and again he reached up and deposited a coin, collected the change, and then with a loud clank he pulled the handle and received his bottle of Coke. He had a Marine knapsack for the bottles, and the little paper package he'd carried out the kitchen door was now spread out on the ground beside him. I couldn't tell what it was for, perhaps it held the change.

Not more than ten minutes had passed when his job was complete. He stood up and looked around him, then hoisted the knapsack over his shoulder, hefting it until it hung just right. Mounting the bike he rode off into the darkness.

I was mystified. I hadn't seen him rob the coin box, only the Cokes. And he'd *paid* for them. I'd heard the coins drop. Waiting until I was sure he was gone, I edged over to the machine. The moon was bright enough now so I could see everything. The coin box was still intact. Not a mark anywhere. I thought for a moment and then knelt down in the same position my man had assumed by the machine only a few moments earlier. And mentally I went through the same operation. I reached down for a coin and felt something hard and round lying there on the frozen ground. A coin, I thought as I brought it up to examine it in the moonlight. It felt strange. Too smooth. And as I looked closely, the coin in my fingers began to *melt*. Ice! That explained the whole thing. Even the water in the coin box . . . and the little paper package of ice quarters which he dropped into the machine, receiving change for each of them of course—a dime and a nickel in cold, hard silver.

I barely made it back to the Academy before the eleven o'clock curfew, but I really didn't care because I had cracked the Coke machine mystery. I dashed up to my room to get cleaned up for my announcement to Big Z. My clothes were so sweaty I had to change. As I was tying my shoes Bruns walked in and I mentioned casually that I'd caught the Coke machine bandit.

"That's just jolly," he said scowling. "By the way, Big Z wants to see you in the SAC's office."

"Fine," I said emphatically. "Because *I* want to see *him*, too."

I was quite confident about the whole thing . . . until I walked into the office and was confronted by the enormous visage of Big Z. His tiny pig's eyes glinted fire. "Hello, there, Mister Ollestad, how was the movie this evening?"

I'd come right to the point. "I didn't go to the movie, I. . . ."

"I know you didn't, Ollestad, that's why I asked to see you."

That damned Robinson, I said under my breath.

"Now tell me, why did you sign out for the theatre if you didn't intend going there in the first place. That kind of thing's liable to make people ask questions, just like I'm doin' now. And we've all learned that questions are dangerous thing, haven't we, Ollestad?"

"Yes, sir, but I had something very important. . . ."

"And what, pray tell, was that?"

*"The Coke machine,"* I blurted, then tried to collect myself. I didn't want to sound like a fool in my moment of triumph.

"I was out on the range tonight . . ."

"So you're the one who's been getting into that machine, huh, Ollestad?"

"Oh, no, sir. I was out there . . . on surveillance," I explained.

"Oh?" said Big Z, stroking a long red scar that sliced around the curve of his chin. His eyes narrowed. "Tell me more."

I took a deep breath. "I found out who did it. I know his *modus operandi* . . . and everything. We can go out right now and. . . ."

"Is that so?" he said coldly.

"Yes, sir. It was one of the colored fellows from the cafeteria. I got his badge number. It was . . ."

"Is that so?" he repeated much louder than before, cutting me off before I could finish. It was plain he didn't want me to continue. "Sit down, Ollestad," he directed. I moved to the seat across from him.

I was incredulous. "Don't you want to know who the thief is?" But my voice cracked and it sounded silly.

"I *know* who it is," he said softly. The big man swiveled around in the chair that belonged to SAC Bone and stared out the window at a platoon of Marines, marching in the moonlight. There was only the rhythmic tattoo of marching feet as they performed an intricate maneuver and then the almost musical cry of the drill instructor as he sang a new command into the night air. Big Z was silent.

Then he swung back to face me, leaning down so his eyes were on the same level with mine. "It's someone who's damned desperate for four bucks! It's someone who knows that if he tries it once or twice he'll get himself caught by one of the sentries on the main road. And meanwhile, Ollestad, I don't need the likes of you to force me into making a detailed report to the Director that would stir up a messy investigation with inspectors crawling in and out of the woodwork and umpteen thousand reports to the Seat of Government—all to explain just why there was a breakdown in the security of an insignificant Coke machine out there in the boondocks more than ten miles from this building! *Do you understand that, Ollestad!*"

It was a command, not a question. And indeed, it took me a moment or two, but I did begin to understand. I realized Big Z was probably right, that the crime really wasn't very important and that a missing handful of nickels and dimes wasn't enough to warrant a whole investigation.

Big Z turned back to the window. I got up to leave. "Whoa, boy, not so fast!" he snarled. His feet were propped up on the window sill and he was watching me over his shoulder. Suddenly his big feet hit the floor and he was actually grinning as he leaned across the desk toward me.

"Yes, sir?"

He jerked his head toward a coffee cup that stood on the edge of his desk. It was filled halfway with coins. Nobody ever smiled at me the way Big Z smiled as he whispered, "I'm sure you understand that we've got to cover the loss to the Coke-man, Ollestad. And your share of it comes to exactly twenty cents."

# 12

The Coke machine caper was a vivid but painful lesson, one that was to have several unexpected and even more painful side-effects. First of all, I'm sure that bicycling through twenty miles of sub-freezing Virginia countryside didn't do me the slightest bit of good, and whether it was psychosomatic or not, right afterwards I came down with the worst cold of my life. And then, as if that were not enough, the good old "family-style food" out at the range cafeteria gave me *food poisoning*.

After the robbery had blown over and it was clear that Big Z had successfully avoided all repercussions from the Seat of Government, SAC Bone returned from leave . . . only to be confronted with the grave problem of sick leave for New Agent Norman T. Ollestad.

Government regulations provided agents with thirteen days annual sick leave with pay, but if we took it we had to explain why, which would set in motion the same ominous and irreversible machinery that Big Z had so recently avoided. There would be letters of explanation to the Seat of Government. Food poisoning at the Quantico Academy? *Unthinkable!* The watchdogs would be upon us in no time. The dread *inspectors*. Heads would roll!

At the time though I was so sick I couldn't have cared what happened, and it was only several days later that I learned they'd solved the problem by not signing me out at all. And in fact one day I qualified with the gas gun out on the range without ever having left my bed!

Actually, I did get out of bed that day—once. And that was to go to the head, but in my stupor I ran straight into the biggest discovery of my Bureau career.

That evening when Bruns came in from the range I started to tell him about it, but at first he was so excited about firing the gas gun I couldn't get a word in edge-wise.

"Honestly, Norm, it was the greatest. Too bad you missed it. You should have seen 'Bu-Lew.' He was a riot. But it was really fun—like Roman candles on the Fourth of July. And it's not as hard as you'd think. . . ." He threw an imaginary gas gun up to his shoulder and demonstrated. "Why I was lobbing those smoke-grenades right on target every time. . . ."

"Looks like I'll never get a chance to qualify," I said.

"You won't have to," said Bruns matter-of-factly. He was by the mirror now, fiddling with a bridge of false teeth that was always giving him trouble.

"What do you mean?"

He moved across the room and sat down on his bed, across from mine, taking a sip from one of the little cups that the Coke machine downstairs dispensed. I cringed. I hadn't noticed the machine before.

"You won't have to qualify," he whispered, "because I watched Big Z fill out a score-card for you, and . . .'" He glanced over his shoulder suddenly. "Hey, did you ever get the feeling this room was *bugged?*"

I sat up. *"Right* . . . that's what I was trying to tell you when you came in." I lowered my voice. "But wait a minute, did you mean that Big Z qualified me out there today?"

"Yeh . . . but don't say anything about it because nobody

, else knows. Hey, what did you mean about the place being bugged?" he whispered. "I was just kidding."

"Well I wasn't. And don't you say anything about this either . . . I've learned my lesson after this Coke machine business."

Bruns nodded appreciatively. "Cheers," he said, toasting me with his cup of coke. "Please continue."

"Well I was pretty woozy this morning and I thought I was going to throw up again and I ran for the head . . . and I don't know what happened really, but somehow I got turned around and ended up going in the wrong door. . . ."

"What's that got to do with the place being bugged?" said Bruns impatiently. He was balancing the cup on one knee now.

"Well I was only there for a minute. Maybe even half a minute, I don't know. But I saw enough to know that right down this hall, inside that room there's a *technical squad.* You know, a wire-tap and tape-recording squad. Electronics stuff was lying around all over the place. Phone-taps, records . . . *everything.* Enough equipment to bug every phone conversation on the East Coast."

"What's there to overhear around here?" he laughed. "It's so dull they'd end up listening in on each other." He was more than dubious.

"That's just the point," I said. "I was there long enough to get a good idea of what was going on, and from what I could overhear they're tapping and recording conversations back in Washington!"

Bruns came suddenly alert. "Hey, do you mean that room right across from the head? The one that's always locked?"

"Why . . . yes."

"I stumbled on it the first day we got here. I wondered

why it was locked up so tight." He paused and swished the coke around in the bottom of the cup. "Sure!" he whispered sharply, pulling closer to me. "That's it! The Justice building would be too obvious for wire-taps . . . the Bureau would *have* to use some out of the way place like this! Hey, this is big stuff. . . ."

"Right," I agreed. "And remember that lecture a few days ago—the one about wire-tapping?"

Bruns nodded.

"Well that little room sure blasts that one all to hell. We're supposed to have only sixty-four phone-taps in operation in the entire country. And they're all supposed to involve the internal security of the country. The only other time we're supposed to use them is in extortion or kidnapping cases and even then only when someone's life is in danger."

"So?" said Bruns.

"So there were more than sixty-four taps in that room alone. Think how many other locked rooms there must be around the country . . . !"

"Forget it," he laughed. "Just be glad you didn't get caught."

"What do you mean? I *did* get caught." Bruns' mouth dropped open and I continued. "One of the agents had gone downstairs for coffee and I guess he forgot to lock the door. And when he got back and found me standing there in my pajamas all hell broke loose."

"Well, come on. Out with it! How did you ever get away?" Bruns was suddenly more excited than I'd ever seen him.

I enjoyed seeing him squirm for once, and I laughed. "I didn't get away, Bill, *I was killed.*"

"No, seriously," said Bruns, ignoring my joke. "What did they do to you?"

"They just gave me a big lecture about internal security and ended up by telling me they wouldn't say anything if I didn't."

"*God!*" said Bruns. "I just happened to think. What if this room is bugged and they overheard us talking about it? We'd really be in hot water! Dammit, Ollestad, if we get nailed for this you'd better cover for me. . . ."

"What do you want me to do . . . call the F.B.I.?"

"That's very funny, Ollestad. . . ."

Bruns was cut short as the door flew open and in marched Keady. "What's that, Ollestad? You lying around here telling jokes?" He glanced around the room. Bruns slid the cup under the bed and I breathed easier. Satisfied everything was in order, the administrator walked over to my bed. "Now if you're telling jokes, Ollestad, you're well enough to resume training, aren't you?"

"Yes, sir," I agreed meekly.

"Fine. It's almost time for dinner. If you want any, I'll be expecting you downstairs." He turned to my roommate, "Mister Bruns, is everything fine with you? We don't want you catching any of this *Ollestad*-sickness that's going around, now do we?"

Bruns stood up. "No, sir," he replied automatically.

"Fine," said Keady and turned toward the door.

Bruns turned toward me and looked relieved, but as he did he accidentally sent the Coca-Cola cup flying under the bed. It came caroming off the wall and stopped dead at my very feet. That's all I need, I thought. There was a pregnant pause. And then without even turning around our administrator marched straight out the door. "See you downstairs, fellows," he said, his footsteps disappearing down the hall. Bruns and I just stared at each other.

As a matter of fact I never did learn for sure whether or not our dorm was bugged. But with Keady's unpredictable comings and goings and the head instructor's anxiety-laden vigilance and Robinson's dormitory intelligence, a little room-bugging wouldn't have made too much difference. We knew we were watched; that was enough to keep us on our toes. And in spite of it all (possibly even because of it) our training rolled along smoothly. We were learning.

But ever since my initial confrontation with Keady in the Justice building men's room on that memorable first day of training, I had wondered why they watched us in the head. That was the one thing that really bothered me. Not once, though, the entire time we were at Quantico did Keady interrupt our washroom reveries. He had a substitute. And it was several days after I'd noticed Keady's absence that I realized the ubiquitous Special Agent Claude Lightfoot was our administrator's relief.

Claude Lightfoot was in his early fifties, but middle-age had done nothing to temper his disposition. He was as fat as he was ornery, and the way he stuck out his lower lip when he got mad he reminded me of the neighborhood sissy everyone beat the stuffing out of when I was a kid. Whenever we ran into him we always got the same nonsensical greeting. "Well hello there, *Charger,*" he growled. His voice was like crushed gravel. "You've got it made, don't you? *Yes sir, you've got it made.*"

I never could figure out what the "You've got it made" bit was all about, until one Saturday afternoon, Claude Lightfoot lost his head.

It was bright and sunny and a bunch of us had organized a game of touch football across the street from the Academy. The snow had melted, turning our field into a regular pigpen. We were covered with mud from head to foot and when we got into a huddle we looked like members of a minstrel show. Our team should have annihilated the competition. We even had one of the instructors on our side, a huge burly chap who'd been a University of Maryland tackle only a few years back. That was our problem. His legendary prowess on the gridiron plus his status as an instructor made him quarterback automatically, even though it was obvious he didn't want the job. But after nearly an hour of end-over-end passes and fumbles on the opposing goal-line I finally suggested that I'd like to throw a few.

"That's a good idea, Ollestad," said the instructor, whose name was Red. "We've had some men in the clear and I haven't been able to hit 'em."

"Wet ball," I suggested.

Red nodded graciously. "Hey—let's all switch around. I'll center . . . and a couple of you guys on the line play back. We'll get the heavies up front . . ." He grabbed the two biggest guys. "You'll be guards . . . and you—*skinny* . . ." He was talking to Bruns, whom I'd always thought of as pretty big, himself. But indeed, beside Red he was . . . skinny.

"Bruns," I said.

"Yeh, Bruns," repeated Red. "You got long legs. You're end. Get the hell down there in back of their defense. Go long! An' Ollestad, you wait till he's all the way there and then hit 'im. We'll keep 'em off ya."

The change was just what was needed. Everybody felt it. And we came out of the huddle yelling. With all that fanfare, I figured I'd better make it good.

For a moment the other team was confused by the change. The backs yelled back and forth trying to figure who to cover. I started calling signals. "Huh-one, huh-two, huh. . . ."

"Hey!" somebody yelled and everything stopped. "What the hell ya doin' over there? Hold it up right there, *Charger!*" It was the head-watcher, Claude Lightfoot. He swaggered across the scrimmage line and straight up to me. "Whatcha think ya doin', Charger?" His lower lip was protruding, and he was madder than hell. He was obviously incensed that a Bureau instructor—particularly one who'd played football at the University of Maryland—was being shoved around by a new agent that weighed less than one hundred and sixty.

I was speechless. I knew that anything I could say would only make him madder. I glanced over at Red. He grinned. "Leave him alone, Claude," he said softly. The agent regarded Red suspiciously. "It's all right, Claude, it was my idea . . . let's get the game going."

"Okay, Red, okay. But I'm warnin' ya. When we get through with him he's gonna look like the St. Valentine's Day Massacre!" Claude Lightfoot turned and waded back through the mud to his own side.

Red turned to me. He was still grinning. "It's okay, don't let him worry you." Then he added, almost as an after-thought, "He's gotta come through me first."

We got back into position and I noticed Lightfoot had switched with his linebacker. And the way he was leaning he telegraphed exactly what he was going to do: He'd sweep around end and try to throw me for a loss.

But there was no time to think. The ball was snapped. I faded back and back. Then suddenly I saw him. He came bolting around Bruns' end and straight for me, his beefy arms outstretched, yelling as he came. Closer and closer . . . then I saw Bruns. He was behind them now. In the clear! I reared back and threw for all I was worth and then braced for the impact . . . when out of nowhere came Red, wading into the screaming demon like an express train. I heard the sickening thud as the two bodies met. And then I saw Bruns running, then diving into the mud, snagging the ball for the touchdown. I started yelling, but it died in my throat as my eyes fell on the motionless Claude Lightfoot stretched out in the mud, stone cold.

In a moment, though, he came to, and his eyes flashed straight into mine and there was no hiding the hate in those eyes, although he could say nothing because the wind was knocked out of him. He just lay there, his chest heaving and his throat making a terrible noise, and I knew if he ever had the chance he'd get even.

He would one day get that chance.

# 13

The firearms instructors were all corn-fed country boys who chewed tobacco constantly (*Day's Work* and *Brown Mule* were their preferred brands) and they possessed that remarkable folk-talent of being able to make a joke out of most anything. And when they discovered I'd never fired any kind of weapon before Quantico they got quite a boot out of it. Their own woodsy brand of logic had led them to believe anyone from California was automatically from Hollywood; and of course anyone from Hollywood just *had* to know all the western movie-heroes, which automatically made me a quick-draw expert and a dead shot able to "knock the eyelash off a squirrel up a tall oak tree" to boot. And even when it turned out otherwise, the name stuck. "Hollywood," I remained.

Actually my inexperience with firearms was an advantage. I hadn't developed any bad habits. I was taught to hold the rifle and shotgun and pistol correctly before firing them, and thus had no tendency to flinch or "buck" shots all over the target like some of the others. And for it I came along faster than any of my classmates, though I was the only one who seemed to think so. Up until the very end of our Quantico training I was always made to fire last with the *goofs,* and among other insufferable indignities they assigned as my partner the incomparable "Bu-Lew."

New Agent Lewis T. Thackery was so nervous about training school and the constant reminders that anyone falling below a B-average would be fired that he actually did all the homework assignments every night. Keady was constantly lauding him for his conscientiousness . . . and in class he was always near the top—and thus he earned the nickname of "Bureau-Lew." But on the range he was terrible. The firing line was no place for nerves, and the way "Bu-Lew" bucked that pistol around he was liable to hit anything. One time or another Lew was credited with direct hits on the cafeteria, the shack where the clay-pigeons for the skeet-range were stored, Big Z's observation tower (a full one hundred eighty degrees from the target area), and the much maligned Coke machine.

When the time finally came for final exams on the firing range, everything went off smoothly. Everyone—even Bu-Lew was firing well . . . until we got to the dueling course. This was the main event in our intra-class competition—but there were serious overtones, too. Chances were that out in the field we'd be firing under "dueling conditions" more than any other. And when the instructors mentioned casually that practice on the dueling course might someday save our lives they were serious.

This was how the dueling course operated: At a given signal a pair of agents began walking side by side and slowly toward the targets, two man-sized pivoting blades whose broad sides flipped around to face the duelists upon the electronic command of an instructor who sat at the control. The agent who drew and fired from the hip and hit his blade was declared the winner of that round. It was strictly an exercise designed to test our reactions and accuracy with the .38 under pressure. Though our service revolvers held six shots, the chamber directly under the hammer was never loaded—to prevent an accidental discharge—and thus there were five rounds to each dueling match.

Even the firearms instructors were excited about the dueling event, and they were so confident they could predict the outcome we were seeded as if it were a tennis tournament. I was given benefit of the doubt over Bu-Lew. He was seeded last; I was next to last. Which of course made us partners for the first duel.

I'll never forget the feeling that morning when word finally came over the loud speaker announcing the first duel between Bu-Lew and Hollywood. Lew and I were led to the ready area by one of the instructors, who handed us our ammunition and ordered us to load.

"Yes indeed," he drawled loud enough for the whole class to hear. "This here's gonna be the duel of the *century!*" The class cheered with mock enthusiasm, but by this time I was used to the instructors' friendly chiding and it didn't bother me.

But as I began slipping the slim copper cartridges into the cylinder my hand began to shake. This was no time to tense up, I told myself. But I couldn't stop. I could feel the sweat trickling down between my shoulder-blades and my hands were clammy. I finally got the cylinder loaded and snapped it shut, glancing up at my partner as I did. He was just inserting the last cartridge when he accidentally hit the ejection mechanism, dumping all five shells onto the ground. The class roared. The instructor knelt down beside Bu-Lew and helped retrieve the cartridges and remained there until the revolver was safely loaded and we were ready to commence.

The signal was given. Bu-Lew and I began walking toward those targets, and I carefully lagged a few feet behind him.

I knew I could out-duel him . . . but with his record I was afraid he might shoot me by mistake.

Luck was with me, though, and I edged him three to two. "Hollywood wins over Bu-Lew," someone cried and they all cheered as if indeed it had been the duel of the century.

Luck would also have it that my second round was with Robinson. By this time the competition was beginning to get tense. Those who had lost weren't saying much, and those who had won were eagerly sizing up the competition. Only the instructors were laughing now and although it was plain they favored Robinson they were pulling for me all the way. But of course no one figured I'd last long. Now they were calling me the "Hollywood long-shot." "Watch out, Robinson," someone yelled, "the Hollywood long-shot is gonna pass you on your blind side!"

"Whadda ya mean?" someone cracked. "He ain't got no blind side. He's got eyes in the back of his head!"

Robinson whipped around trying to identify who'd said it. I tried to keep from laughing. It must have been one of the instructors. They all smiled.

Then came the signal to begin. We walked toward those blades. I wasn't so tense now. I'd discovered that an extra beat after I drew helped establish a rhythm and steadied my hand, and although even Bu-Lew had beat me to the target twice I had yet to miss. That was my strategy—I'd take my chance about beating Robinson to the draw; I'd just make damned sure I hit that target every time. I knew everyone expected me to lose, but I just couldn't. Not to Robinson.

Suddenly the blades flipped. Robinson beat me to the draw and fired wildly. Missed! The bullet ricocheted off the asphalt beneath his blade and was still singing off somewhere into the countryside when I fired and the light on my side flashed and the buzzer rang telling everyone that the first round was *mine*.

But my opponent learned quickly. The next round he took a fraction of a second longer and his light flashed first. The next round, too. But I grabbed the fourth, firing an instant before him, and now it was evened up. Two and two. The last round coming up.

"Come on you Hollywood long-shot," someone yelled. Robinson shot me a dirty look. A moment passed and we got the signal . . . and then an eternity as step by step we inched closer to those blades. I wasn't nervous anymore. Just taut, like a wire spring. Exhilarated. I saw everything, heard everything—the tiny pebbles in the asphalt beneath the target, the trees on the hillside beyond us, the wind and Robinson's breathing and my own heart pounding as we stepped closer and closer . . . then they flipped! And I was right there with them—crouched, drawing and firing all in one movement. But Robinson was there, too. And both of us fired together, both buzzers buzzing and both lights flashing at the same time, and we all stood around looking at each other.

There was a silent moment as everybody realized what happened. It was plainly a draw. But when I turned and looked toward the instructors and saw the bewilderment written even on their faces I realized there could be no draw. The rules provided only for a double miss, in which case we could re-load and fire until one man finally hit. But this was *not* a double miss. One man had to be declared the winner, and it was almost as if everyone realized it at the same time, for we all looked up in unison toward the man at the control, the agent in charge who would make that decision—Big Z.

Well that does it, I said to myself. If there was a decision to be made it would most surely not be in my favor—not if

Big Z had anything to do with it. Not after blasting him over the head with his own blackjack . . . and the Coke machine caper, and the food poisoning . . . and I knew damned well he'd heard about my blundering into that room on the third floor. I glanced at Robinson. He gazed back confidently. No sir, I hadn't a ghost of a chance.

"*Ollestad.* . . ." It was the loud-speaker. I whipped around and gazed up at Big Z who had the microphone up to his mouth and was busily thumbing through some papers, apparently looking for something, completely unconcerned with the burden of deciding between us. "Just a minute, Ollestad . . . let's see that puts you together with Bruns. That ought to make a pretty good match. . . ."

He said it matter-of-factly—as if it were completely obvious to everyone that I'd won—and I didn't understand at first. It was only when I turned to Robinson and saw the hatred written on his face that I realized Big Z had through some miracle decided in my favor.

I had beat New Agent Thomas Robinson, and for the moment that seemed like the most important thing in the world. But now I was in the third round of competition where only six out of our class of twenty-two remained, and I suddenly realized what little chance I had of even placing in the dueling event. Ahead of me were Bruns . . . and then even assuming I beat him, which was highly doubtful, there were Barrow, Wright and Bedner, the instructors' favorites. I had no chance.

But this was my lucky day. I scraped by Bruns three to two (after he was disqualified for jumping the gun on the last shot) and then to everyone's amazement I blanked Barrow five to nothing. Now nobody laughed. And when I squeezed by Wright by a single point I could see from the instructors' tight-lipped expressions they were plainly irritated. They took their dueling seriously.

It was okay when I beat Bu-Lew. They'd expected that. And I'm sure everyone was glad when I beat Robinson. But Barrow and Wright were an entirely different matter: these were "good huntin' country boys" who'd learned Kentucky windage before I could read and write, and who'd spent their summers in the blue-grass country hunting coon and 'possum while I was breaking my right arm trying to perfect my fastball. No, it didn't make sense to anyone that *Hollywood* was in the finals with New Agent Michael Bedner, better known as the "Arkansas Traveler." It just wasn't right. And they held up the finals until after lunch.

In the cafeteria all tension vanished and the instructors were once again their jovial selves, and they actually made a big ceremony out of the normally drab noon meal. We were both made to sit at the head of the table and great portions of that famous "home-style food" were heaped before us, until I secretly wondered if they were trying to poison me again. I was so nervous my appetite completely disappeared, while the Arkansas Traveler was as cool as ice and joked with me throughout the entire meal. I thought perhaps he regarded me as another Bu-Lew and was only trying to calm me down so I wouldn't shoot him by mistake.

Once back on the range, though, the instructors' coolness toward me returned. They made no bones about it. They simply ignored me. And while two of them went about the business of setting up the course the other pair hovered about the Traveler like seconds in a boxing match, pantomiming their own personal stratagems and joking back and forth to keep their champion relaxed. He hardly needed it. When we stepped up to the line together he flashed me a friendly grin as if we'd known each other for years.

"Ah hear they got steak for dinner tonight," he drawled unexpectedly. "Let's get this duelin' business over with." He was as cool as a breezy summer day down south.

We got the signal and started toward the targets. I'd noticed Big Z had been standing close by where he could get a better view of the dueling this time, and I didn't know who was at the control but whoever it was waited longer than he was supposed to and I nearly disqualified myself by jumping the gun. And when the blades finally did flip I was caught amid-stride and off rhythm and I bucked the shot way off target, and from the little puff of dust on the asphalt it looked like I came closer to the Traveler's target than my own. The Traveler squeezed one off for an easy first point.

Apparently he'd noted my wild first shot and when the blades turned the next time he waited for me to buck one into the hillside—which I did! But before he had a chance to squeeze off another easy win I jerked off a second shot and my buzzer rang an instant before his. We were even, one and one. But I only had two shots left.

I let the Traveler fire first on the next one and pulled the hammer all the way back to full cock, planning to squeeze one off slow and easy after he missed—but he didn't miss. On the next round I was lucky and clipped the bare edge of the blade, but the buzzer rang and the light flashed and we were even up, two and two. At least I'd be able to say I took him all the way down to the last shot.

Now there was dead silence. We were right on top of them. We couldn't miss. Whoever drew first had it. I could feel every muscle in my body tense . . . and then I heard the click of the target mechanism and the blades flipped and the Traveler fired even before I'd cleared my holster, and I figured that was it. I stared at the blades now no more than ten feet away, and there was no sound. No buzzing. Only the echo of the Traveler's shot as the sound rebounded from the far off hills. He missed! All I had to do was squeeze the trigger and I was the winner.

The whole class, the instructors, and the Arkansas Traveler stood by incredulous as I slid back the hammer and squeezed the trigger and braced for that final grand explosion—but somehow instead of the explosion there came only a feeble click. The hammer struck the rim of the cartridge and failed to fire. Fumbling and cursing, I did my best to spin the cylinder around and fire that round again—as the Traveler went coolly about his business. He loaded an extra round and fired it easily into the center of the target and walked off with the victory that was so nearly mine.

"Come on, Hollywood," he said, grabbing me by the shoulder. "Let's go get us that steak dinner."

The firearms instructors never said a word to me about the dueling match or about my overall performance on the range (I placed fifth) which I was pretty proud of, considering they'd pegged me near the bottom of the class. But several weeks later, at the conclusion of training school and just as we were about to be sent out into the field, we were issued our revolvers. And somehow I was the one who received a brand new *Smith & Wesson .38*—the only unused weapon issued to the New Agents' Class.

"The [Communist] Party, in many respects, is a vast paternalistic system."

J. Edgar Hoover, *Masters of Deceit*

# 14

It was only when NAC had returned to the Seat of Government for our final few weeks of training that I fully realized how different our training at the Quantico Academy had been. Now our classes, our instructors, our whole routine seemed suddenly dull, and although we were once again permitted to go out on weekends, Bruns and I found that we tired easily of our old haunts. Even our Georgetown acquaintances were unamusing. They still told the same old jokes and fabricated the same thread-bare arguments and they still turned off the lights and tumbled around with the same dull girls. But something was different. We had changed.

I had learned. Looking back on the Coke machine caper, the food-poisoning incident, the dueling match and the locked-room affair, the whole thing was amusing—on the surface. But down deep I knew Quantico had taught me the most serious lessons of my Bureau career. I now understood that in the face of day to day disasters silence was indeed a virtue. Yes, there was more to this man's Bureau than met the eye.

I had also pretty much decided that our administrator and a good many of the other instructors were running scared, with only the successful conclusion to twenty years of Bureau service at the end of the string. They were frightened men who lived in constant dread of the Director. It was obvious to me that the reason they were so afraid was that they lived within the letter of his law rather than by its spirit. Big Z was of course an exception, although even he had once proclaimed: "Take care of the little things and the big things will take care of themselves." At the time I had no idea just how right he was.

But my enlightenment did little to make the training pass faster. By this time we were so close to graduation that it was hard for us to think of anything else. Night and day we dreamed of the field. At NAC we had learned the rules; at Quantico we'd been given a chance to practice. In the field we would play the game.

One morning we walked into class to find Keady already there and waiting at the podium. His hair was freshly combed, his shoes sparkled and he looked more lively than usual and for the first time I could remember he looked confident.

"Sit down, fellows, sit down," he said eagerly. I glanced at the clock. Only five till nine. It probably wasn't anything important, although Keady had always arrived right at the stroke of nine. Mildly curious, Bruns and I found our seats, prepared for another uninspiring lecture.

"Fellows, I have just come from the Director's office," he announced even before the class was settled. We were thunderstruck. The Director's office. What could that mean? We were suddenly very wide awake.

"Word has just been received from Quantico," he continued, "and I am pleased to announce that we all did pretty well in our examinations. *Very* well in fact. All above average grades. Fellows—we all passed!"

Our administrator beamed. A sigh of relief came from the class.

What did they expect? I muttered under my breath. Everybody knew our exams at Quantico were rigged just as they always had been rigged here. The big question in my mind was how did it all get by the Director? But I guessed he had more important things to worry about. I'd been reading in the papers that Attorney General Kennedy was marshaling his forces for an all-out war on organized crime. And despite their personal differences the Director was still the attorney general's right-hand man. God, how I wanted out into the field!

Keady droned on for another few minutes and ended up congratulating himself for our outstanding performance at Quantico. "Fellows, I am proud to have led you through the last three months of training successfully. I know that some of the material may have seemed redundant at times, but now you can readily understand why certain subjects were emphasized. Inevitably they were the ones that appeared on the exams. Today I am going to talk briefly about several key issues—civil rights, communism, juvenile delinquency, and the KGB. You won't be tested on them again . . . but there is another even *more* important reason for your close attention."

Without bothering to explain that enigma, Keady poured out the same stagnant information on communism and juvenile delinquency that he had immersed us in at least a dozen times before. I tried to keep my mind from wandering off into fantasies of the field, but it was almost impossible.

I nudged my roommate. "Hey," I whispered, "wake me up when he gets to the KGB part." That was the Soviet secret police force and I wanted to be sure to learn everything there was to know about them.

"Why bother?" he yawned. "You've heard the same old stuff a thousand times. Wait until you get out into the field. Then you'll learn about the KGB and about ten thousand other things they'll never teach you here . . ."

"Like what?"

"Oh . . . little things. Like the wire-tapping stuff . . . and like the agents who live across the street from the Russian embassy."

"What agents?"

"Oh, I forgot. You wouldn't know about them yet. They've lived there for years. All they do is take telephoto pictures of everyone who walks in and out of the Russian embassy. That's their whole job. . . ."

Suddenly Bruns lurched upright in his seat, stopping short in mid-sentence. For an instant I didn't know what had happened. Then I realized Keady had stopped talking and was staring down directly at us.

"Now Mister Bruns," Keady began tiredly. "I'm sure that as a former Bureau clerk there is much that you might tell us. Would you like to step up here and explain what it is that you and Mister Ollestad find so fascinating while I am speaking?"

Bruns remained poker-faced and silent. But Keady would not let it pass.

"Come, come, Bruns. What is it?"

Pressed, Bruns had to answer. He shot bolt upright to attention, his eyes riveted on Keady who himself looked not a little surprised at his directness as Bruns began loudly and distinctly. "Yes, sir. You had just been speaking of the linked problems of juvenile delinquency and the CPUSA and you applied the words of our Director. I believe they were: 'The CPUSA has continued its unswerving allegiance to the Soviet Union, which is committed to the goal of world-wide domination by communism.' And you pointed out that it is only fuzzy-thinking liberals who contend the Communist party is dead in this country . . .

"And then, sir, I must confess that I turned to Mister Ollestad and commented that the only reason CPUSA membership has shrunk from its high of eighty thousand in the nineteen-thirties to less than seven thousand today is that since the Smith Act and the Dennis Decision the party has been forced underground."

"Ah yes indeed, Mister Bruns," said Keady basking in the sweet sound of his own words, "as you well know the party is stronger now than ever." Keady rambled on quoting the same shopworn information about communism. It soon grew apparent that Bruns' diversionary tactic had been completely successful.

Sometime later Bruns nudged me as our administrator flipped over his notes and set about describing the KGB. But it was the same tired information we had been given time and time again, and Bruns looked over and grinned as if to say I told you so. I couldn't do as well as Bruns, parroting the whole spiel word for word, but I could recall much of it verbatim. Only the names hung me up a little. Vladimir Senichastgvy—that was sure a mouthful. He was head of the KGB and he took his orders from Mikhail Suslov, Communist party ideologist, and from Nikolai Podgorny, head of the party's Internal Security Commission.

An hour later Keady concluded. "Now fellows, don't get

the idea that there is any similarity between the F.B.I. and the KGB. They have more than half a million agents as compared to our six thousand. . . . But there's a much more important difference. They have absolutely no understanding of constitutional police methods.

"And another thing. The public isn't aware of it, but there are many KGB agents operating here in the U.S., many of them right here in Washington—in government positions! Since early 1960 more than two hundred highly trained KGB assassins have shown up in western countries, all of them equipped with the latest weapons and the most modern techniques in espionage. Actually, though, the Director is most concerned with their techniques of implanting pro-Soviet ideologies into western literary publications, the devastating effects of which are only too plainly obvious."

At that point there was a mysterious air of finality to the way Keady snapped shut his notebook and walked down slowly from the speaker's platform. Was he through? He couldn't be. There was at least an hour of class left before lunch. I couldn't get over the administrator's newfound confidence.

"Fellows, I was going to wait until this afternoon, but I might as well tell you now. Tomorrow is the big day. . . ." Keady gazed from one quizzical face to another, plainly enjoying our suspense. "That's right, fellows—the Big Day."

He had us completely mystified. Bruns, who had spent the last fifteen minutes drowsily examining his fingernails watched closely, his brow furrowed.

"What's he talking about, Bill?" I whispered, but Bruns stared straight ahead, giving no sign that he'd heard me.

Keady had played this game before and I figured he'd probably string us along for awhile. Maybe even the rest of the day. It probably wasn't anything very important any-way. Once at Quantico he'd kept us guessing an entire day, and only at the conclusion of class was his secret revealed: *The F.B.I. Story* was playing at the base movie theater. (That, of course, was the night of the infamous Coke machine caper.)

Our administrator surprised me when he marched back up to the platform and began erasing the blackboard and with his back still turned began speaking as casually as he had announced the movie at Quantico. "Fellows, tomorrow morning at eight-thirty . . . we will all assemble here to pre-pare. . . ." He paused. Beneath his confidence I detected something a little too casual—like he was straining. And as he turned to face us and he began anew he almost lost con-trol.

"Tomorrow we're going to meet the Director!"

At first we were stunned. So that was it. We had passed the exams. The meeting with the Director was the last step, the most crucial one of all.

"Today we've got to make sure you understand everything we've talked about here in class and that you've really learned everything that has been on those exams." For the next few moments he remained bent over the podium, searching through his notes.

I couldn't believe it. That was almost an admission that the exams had been fakes. Now it was clear. He hadn't told us about the meeting with the Director right off simply be-cause it was good showmanship to tell us later. If he appeared calm, then we, too, would appear confident before the Direc-tor. Beneath, he was probably worried sick, but he dared not show it. But at the same time he wanted to make sure we knew the material—and to do that he had to worry us a little. I wasn't at all sure our administrator could weather the strain of such a powerful paradox.

The performance continued. "Now all that material I gave you this morning . . . well, I don't have to remind you that you must know it thoroughly. It's all in your notes; you've heard it before. So for the rest of our time today I'm going to concentrate on getting you ready for the meeting itself.

"He . . . the Director usually gives us more warning than this, b-but word has it that he's particularly interested in this class." I wondered what that meant. It was obvious Keady didn't know either for he made no more mention of it. The thought flashed through my mind that the Director might have heard about some of the "irregularities" in our class. Maybe even about the Coke machine or the wire-tapping room . . . maybe he wanted to get information out of us. I was beginning to get nervous, too.

In the past, whenever our administrator grew more concerned than usual he came up with a slogan; ritual always seemed to somehow pacify him, and today he coined a dandy. "Now there's one thing we can count on tomorrow," he said happily. "Our Director is consistent right down the line. And as he always says, 'Consistency is the best policy.' "

Bruns glanced at me and we both smiled secretly. Now we knew exactly where we stood. All but the Director's interest in our class. That still had me mystified. But from Keady's "consistency" remark, we knew that by tomorrow morning at eight-thirty we would be amply prepared for the Director, just as we'd been prepared for the examinations. "Consistency" meant that the meeting was Bureau ritual, that the mechanics were predictable, and the outcome simply depended upon Keady's ability to teach us, our ability to learn and perform the catechism.

Now Keady turned to the blackboard. Slowly and elaborately he began printing the names of each of the twenty-two members of NAC on the blackboard. The class was hushed as he did so. They were plainly not in alphabetical order, nor any kind of discernible order for that matter, and we all stared as if our administrator was constructing some sort of conundrum to test our reason. My name was toward the middle; I didn't know whether I should feel good or bad about it.

I'm sure we were all relieved when he put down the chalk and explained. "What I have listed here is the order by which we shall proceed into the Director's office. You will notice that the taller men have been placed at the extreme ends of the line, at the beginning and at the end, while the men of average height will fill out the middle. Now the point of all this is to make it easier on the shorter men . . ." Keady shot a piercing look at Robert Barrow who sat squirming and self-conscious at the rear of the class. He brushed away an imaginary fly and tried to look unconcerned. Inches under the announced minimum height for F.B.I. agents, Barrow always did his best to be inconspicuous, though with his spectacular set of nerves he seldom succeeded. He would be camouflaged. His place was number eleven.

"Now a word about proper attire. A man from the last class was dismissed for not wearing the right clothes. Like Ollestad there he wore striped shirts. This is not Hollywood, fellows, it's the Federal Bureau of Investigation, and young businessmen of the Bureau are expected to wear conservative business suits, white shirts and dark socks. And stay away' from button-down collars. Only left-wing liberals wear them. Oh, yes—and striped ties. The Director doesn't care for them at all. But he does demand that his agents wear handkerchiefs. They should protrude exactly one-half inch from the pocket, should be folded perfectly straight across. No points.

"Now about good grooming. That's one thing that's very important to the Director, for as he often says, 'Efficiency, good grooming, and free enterprise determine who gets ahead and who gets left by the wayside in the F.B.I.' " Keady rummaged around in his briefcase as he spoke, finally withdrawing three cardboard, hand-painted charts. They were well worn. For a moment they looked like clumsy portraits of a short-haired Rudolph Valentino. Then I noticed that in each the hair was combed differently.

"The right haircut is basic to good grooming," said Keady indicating the portraits.

A murmur of disapproval came from the rear of the class.

Keady was immediately on the defensive. "Look, fellows, it's just common sense. Only high school gigolos wear their hair long; and college book-worms wear it short. Young businessmen of the Bureau wear it one of these three ways. And another thing, as long as we're on the subject of haircuts, the Director doesn't like bald-headed agents. They destroy our image."

"I know there's nothing you can do about it if you are growing prematurely bald . . ." He smiled and bent his own respectable head of hair down for our inspection, and if you looked closely you could see he had very cleverly concealed a tiny bald-spot with a few strategically placed strands of hair. "But if you have an area where the hair is simply thin, such as I have," he confided, "make sure you keep it covered up.

"Another thing. The Director doesn't like mustaches either, so don't leave anything lying around on your face tomorrow that might be mistaken for one. John Dillinger wore a mustache, fellows, and you *know* what happened to him!"

Next Keady picked up a long cardboard cylinder that had been standing upright by the podium, and from it he extracted and unrolled a large paper which he pinned to the board. It looked like the floorplan to a building or a part of a building. And sure enough, Keady picked up his pointer and indicated the central area of the diagram and said, "This is the interior layout of the Director's office. Over here is the outer office . . . and here is the exterior door.

"Tomorrow morning, precisely at nine, we will walk in that door, where we will be met by Sam, the Director's colored receptionist." Keady stepped forward and briefed us on the receptionist and his responsibilities to the Director. The whole thing was getting exciting now. The meeting with the Director was being planned just like an important Bureau operation—which of course it was.

"As soon as we get there, Sam will walk into the inner office to announce us. We will be kept waiting in the outer office for exactly fifteen minutes. And we will wait quietly— but don't just stand there in our pre-arranged line. Mix around the room, *casually*. Just keep in mind who is on either side of you so you can return to your proper place when the time comes.

"You won't have to worry about Sam, he won't give you any trouble. The old nigger will mumble a lot and you won't understand a word he says. He'll just cluck around like an old black crow. He's been with the Director for years . . . and he's a Bureau employee just like you and me. Treat him like you would anyone else." Keady looked up sharply. "Just don't let me catch any of you shaking hands with him. . . ."

Our administrator was aware that those last words had

rung a hollow note. Not wanting to create a need for further explanation he retreated to his briefcase and began hunting for the next exhibit.

With each new exhibit our excitement mounted. Now as Keady retrieved a glossy photograph from his briefcase the class leaned forward, eagerly anticipating this new bit of information as if their lives might depend upon it. Keady carefully pinned the photograph between the office diagram and hair-style charts and then pulled back to make sure it was straight.

He stepped aside proudly. "Fellows . . . this is the *Director.*" His tone was almost reverent, almost as if he were introducing the flesh and blood man himself.

Picking up his pointer, Keady then proceeded to brief us on the vital statistics, treating the Director every bit as analytically as he did the floor-plan of his office.

"Fellows, a recent report describes our Director as 'just under six feet tall.' Actually, he is about five feet nine inches in height, though he looks to be a much bigger man. His official weight is one hundred sixty-eight pounds . . . but from time to time, when the press of business doesn't allow him his daily walk he might shoot up to two hundred, but only briefly. Our last minute report pegs him close to one-ninety."

Keady turned back to the diagram. "Now as we enter, the Director will be standing beside his government-issue desk." He indicated a point on the diagram toward the center of the Director's inner office. "Walk up to him briskly, look him directly in the eye, and greet him in a clear, well modulated voice. I'll get to the proper greeting in a moment. The Director speaks very precisely, and later this afternoon an inspector who is familiar with his splendid delivery will let us listen to some tapes and help us practice the greeting.

"Now as you greet the Director he will extend his right hand—but don't extend yours until he does so. Then as his hand moves toward yours give it a nice, firm grip. You may use one of three approved greetings . . ." Keady withdrew a sheet of paper and read from it. "You may say 'Good morning, Mister Hoover, my name is . . .' or you may say 'Pleased to meet you, Mister Hoover, my name is . . .' or you may say 'How do you do, Mister Hoover, my name is . . .' Of course you will insert your own name in the proper place, but there will be no deviations from these three greetings. They have been tested hundreds of times and nothing ever happened." Keady struck the side of the podium with his pointer for emphasis. "I repeat: There will be no deviations. Is that clear? Don't even think of trying anything clever—it might just hit him wrong and poof!" Our administrator clapped his hands to make a tiny explosion. Everyone got his meaning.

"The greeting and handshake—and in fact the entire meeting should not exceed thirty seconds per man, but while you're in there, there are three distinct dangers. First, as you enter you will encounter a thick carpet, so don't scuff your feet. And whatever you do *don't look down*. Occasionally, our Director enjoys standing on a little box when he greets people in his office. Of course, it's just a small one, only six inches high. Pretend you never even noticed it! Not long ago we had a new agent who for some reason just couldn't keep his eyes off it. He was *fired*."

Our administrator proceeded to the next point. "The second danger," he announced with an ominous ring, "is the Director's bathroom."

I was startled. Bruns smiled. That was a new one on us both.

"If the Director asks you a question, be sure and keep your wits about you; otherwise, move out of there as fast as you can—take your leave and make sure you don't veer off course on your way out this door." He pointed to a mark on the diagram that indicated a doorway. "This door is fine; it leads to the outer hallway. But this one. . . ." He indicated another doorway. "Well it leads to the Director's private bathroom. Nobody else is allowed in there, and if one of you got in there by mistake . . . who knows what might happen? There's no way out except back through the office." The threat of getting trapped in the Director's toilet shook him visibly.

Indicating the rear of the Director's office, our administrator pushed on to the third and final danger. "Fellows, while you're shaking the Director's hand you are also being watched by Associate Director Christman who always attends these meetings. He stands here," said Keady indicating a tiny cross on the diagram, "right by this window where he can see you from a different angle. He is known to be very critical of new agents. The associate director gives his impressions of each man to the Director, so you don't want to irritate him by staring at him or looking down at the Director's box. Don't forget it—Christman can see *everything*."

# 15

That night I stayed up until well after midnight, polishing my shoes and reviewing my notes, while Bruns as usual went to bed early. I was almost as eager to meet the Director as I was to get out into the field. J. Edgar Hoover, the man, stood for everything an agent should be. The man was old, certainly, but it was young men such as myself who would carry on the traditions of the F.B.I., the heritage of our Director. And it was for men like Robinson to become the Keadys and Farmers of the future.

As Keady had so often reminded us, we were *young business-men of the Bureau*—and the F.B.I. was big business. Before we might function as *executives in this nationwide business of law enforcement* we had to learn the rules. Without them the Bureau would tumble into chaos. But there was something more important—beyond the rules. Once we had been trained, once we had proven we understood the principles—once order was established, we might proceed out into the field as individuals. Yes, I was anxious to meet the Director. That meeting would mark my own acceptance as a special agent of the F.B.I.

The morning came. The alarm went off and our tiny window to the outside world was still pitch black. Outside the mists still hung heavy as we set out through deserted streets for the Justice building. We figured the walk would relax us, although it would take the better part of an hour.

We had to leave doubly early if we wanted breakfast before Keady's eight-thirty briefing.

And indeed the walking was good. Over the past few months silence had grown strangely alien. Malibu was the only quiet place I could remember. I was still thinking of home as Bruns and I together with a handful of classmates hurried through the swinging doors of the Justice building and down the strangely deserted hallways, avoiding as we went the little piles of debris built by the janitors. They were hurrying, too. The halls had to be clean and ready by nine.

We walked into class and there was Keady already prepared for us. The charts were back on the board alongside the glossy photograph of the Director. I glanced at the podium at the head of the classroom.

"Look, Bill," I said.

Bruns was taken aback. "Looks like we've got our own janitorial service," he whispered. Over the podium a white towel was spread like a tablecloth, on which our administrator had neatly arranged all the accoutrements of a well stocked toilet kit.

Yes, we too would be ready by nine.

While Keady was examining each new agent from the top of his well barbered head right down to the soles of his glistening dress shoes, we had visitors. Several agents whom I'd seen around the Academy at various times wandered in casually. I figured they were merely curious. But Bruns informed me quietly they were inspectors. Our meeting with the Director was important all right. Not only to us but to everyone in the Academy.

Keady looked me over. He was plainly relieved that I'd worn a plain white dress shirt for the occasion. I'd seen fit to get my hair cut the night before in the Roosevelt barber shop. But my frugal roommate elected to save two dollars and Keady was nearly fit to be tied until Bruns finally allowed him to snip off a few hairs that brushed past his ears.

I checked my watch against the classroom clock. At three minutes to nine one of the inspectors walked over and whispered to our administrator. Thirty seconds later we assembled into our pre-arranged line, and after a final last-second check by Keady we streamed out into the hallway behind him.

It was precisely nine o'clock when we marched into the Director's outer office. No one said a word. As per Keady's instructions we mixed around the room, but it looked awkward. Like boy's choice at a grade school cotillion.

Sam was there as anticipated. Everything was exactly as Keady had described it. The receptionist mumbled a few pleasantries which the administrator acknowledged coldly and in a moment he disappeared into the Director's inner office. It was three minutes after nine.

It was a small room, not much space for twenty-two new agents to browse around in. At one end stood a bookcase which housed an elegantly bound collection of what appeared to be law books. On top was an assortment of photographs. Moving closer, I noticed that most were of the Director, posed with various distinguished looking men. And I recognized a few as past presidents. *"The Director has served seven Presidents . . ."* echoed somewhere in my memory. In many of the pictures the Director appeared as a young man, not much older than myself, wearing an old-fashioned suit. I'd forgotten how long he'd been with the F.B.I. *"On August first nineteen-nineteen our Director was first associated with the Bureau. . . ."* Again the words stood out in my memory. We'd heard them so many times we couldn't possibly forget them. Over forty years of service, as Director of the F.B.I.

Bruns browsed by and glanced at my watch. Ten minutes after nine. Tension was mounting. Bruns winked and pretended to absorb himself in a glass-topped display case. I followed his lead. The first thing I noticed was something that resembled a plaster casting of a man's face. An identification card propped beneath the chin proclaimed: "Death mask, John Dillinger, 1934."

I browsed from case to case, peering in at the scores of various kinds of weapons, trophies that represented stellar moments in Bureau history. I stopped for a moment before a case that held a badly corroded pair of brass knuckles. The card identified them as having belonged to none other than "Pretty Boy" Floyd.

Suddenly someone brushed my arm and I looked up into the nervously searching eyes of our administrator. "Careful, Ollestad," he whispered, "we can't be leaving any fingerprints around on these glass cases." Before I had a chance to see if he was serious or not he had fled to the aid of my roommate whose necktie was slightly askew. But then Bruns was first in line. He had to be perfect.

It was thirteen after nine when the door to the Director's inner office opened, then closed again softly. It was Sam. He had been gone exactly ten minutes. Keady stared at him questioningly.

The Negro smiled. "Been quite awhile since ah seen you 'round heah, Mistuh Keady suh. . . ."

The administrator frowned. "I was here yesterday morning, if you'll remember," he replied curtly.

There was an awkward silence. Keady glanced at his watch. It was nine fifteen. He turned back to Sam and started to say something, but Sam just nodded his head up and down, smiling happily. There was no buzzer, no signal from the inner office. He didn't even have a watch. Sam just knew. "Yassuh, Mistuh Keady suh, if you' folks is ready you can go right on in now. The Director's ready fo' y'all."

It took only a few seconds for us to fall into line. Keady surveyed us briefly, then followed Sam into the Director's office. He reappeared in an instant and led Bruns inside. The door closed slowly behind them. The meeting had begun.

First Bruns, then Tom Rettis. . . . I was number eight. At thirty seconds each that left me a little less than four minutes. I imagined Bruns inside, shaking hands with the Director: at that very moment, looking him straight in the eye. I had to hand it to Bruns. He might not have been to law school like the rest of us, but he sure did have a cool head on his shoulders.

It took Bruns exactly twenty-five seconds. I knew he'd be all right. But Rettis was one of the nervous ones. He might have trouble. Suddenly I was aware of a low mumbling behind me and I turned only to look full into the acned face of Thomas Robinson. I'd forgotten he was number nine. He acknowledged me with a nervous twitch of his mouth. His right hand gripped a neatly folded handkerchief which he used to sop up his perspiring palm. The Director didn't like moist, clammy handshakes. His eyes fled back to a 4 x 5 card that he held in his left hand. Apparently it contained notes. The mumbling resumed again and I turned around and ignored it.

Somehow my mind drifted back to my senior year in high school where I'd stood in a line exactly like this one, only it was for my football physical. I'd been just as nervous and excited. Then came that moment when the coach and our team physician looked at my left knee, the one I'd spent the whole year exercising and strengthening and getting in shape for the big season . . . but it was hopeless. They just shook their heads and went on to the next man. I could not play.

Then I was standing at the door to the Director's office and I realized I was next and I had the same terrible feeling in my stomach. What if the same thing happened here?

The seconds dragged by. Then without warning the door jerked open and Robinson's mumbling died in his throat as Keady motioned me inside frantically. I smiled what must have been a nervous smile and edged past him. His face was stone.

The door eased shut. And then there was that thick carpeting beneath my feet, every bit as luxurious as our administrator had promised, and that was fine. My eyes jumped mechanically to the center of the room where Keady's floorplan had pin-pointed the Director's government-issue desk. I panicked! *It wasn't there.* But somehow in that soundless pandemonium my eyes found the desk toward the rear of the room, somehow strangely apart from it all with a long empty space between the desk and the rear wall. And there beside the desk, motionless, watching my every move, stood the Director, J. Edgar Hoover.

I launched myself across the room, taking great pains not to stumble on the carpet, but as my eyes fastened to the eyes of the Director the whole scene speeded up like an old time cinema. For an instant a dark shape hovered there by him. Christman? Then he was there by the window and I knew that it was Christman, a big ancient bird, a crusty old pelican looking for fish. No—an *eagle.* That was better. He even smiled a little. A beady-eyed Department of Justice eagle who smiled without his lips.

The room was large and comfortable, more like someone's study or a large den than it was an office. I came closer. To the rear of him were photos and a massive brass pistol lamp and there was that gleaming mahogany, government-issue desk and then the man himself as I stopped before that desk and the man extended his hand—*the Director*.

The greeting, the handshake—the meeting was all automatic, just as planned. I performed the catechism, staring all the while up into the hard brown eyes of the man. The face was impossible, like papier-mâché, and much older than any of the photographs revealed—but there was a strength in those hard eyes and in his hand as we exchanged a firm Bureau handshake that would have made our administrator proud. And it was all over in less than half a minute.

I was grateful. There were no questions. And despite all admonitions there was no special interest in our class, for ours was like countless other classes that have passed through training, met the Director, and then passed on into the field. I took my leave, carefully avoiding the forbidden door to the Director's private bathroom and passed calmly out into the hallway where it suddenly dawned on me that I'd forgotten to look for the little box! But I had looked up to him, so he must have been standing on something, for according to Keady's last minute statistics we were both five feet nine inches tall. Whatever the source, our Director was indeed *a much bigger man*.

The meeting had gone off exactly as planned. The Director was consistent. All machinery functioned smoothly. For this alone everyone was thankful. But for me the meeting had given rise to some perplexing questions.

Fifteen minutes in the outer office and thirty seconds before the man himself had done it. In that office the photographs and mementos lined the walls, filling their glass cases with a musty aura I would not soon forget. Even the man himself was much older than I'd realized. But forty years on the job was a long time for any man. And the man *should* look old, that was only human. Why then had we been shown a photo that was more than twenty years old? The trophies were old, too, most of them dating from the twenties and thirties. Why none of a more modern vintage? Why none of the *Cosa Nostra?* Why only the relics of days long past when the Director was but a single man and crime was a one-man operation? Modern crime was big business. So was the F.B.I.

But they were only questions. Far from disillusioned, I knew more than ever that Bruns was right: there was much to learn, even though our days of training were nearly done. More than ever our Director needed young men like myself out in the field. Young men who would one day win new up-to-date trophies for the F.B.I. I secretly vowed to supply some new additions to that trophy room as soon as they cut me loose with a badge and gun. Indeed, that very night I dreamed that there was a photo standing proudly in that office—a photo of Special Agent Norman T. Ollestad shaking hands with none other than the Director, John E. Hoover.

But the days of training were *not* yet done, and in the next few days I was to learn things I probably shouldn't have known about even after twenty years in the field. The very next day in fact I once again shook hands with the Director.

It was the five o'clock rush hour and Bruns and I were waiting for the elevator on the fourth floor of the Justice building. When it finally arrived there was barely room for us but we hardly noticed and we squeezed aboard. Everyone seemed unusually silent. The elevator made its usual noisy descent, lurched over the last few feet, then rocked to a halt at the ground floor. It always did that. But today it caught Bruns off balance and he swayed into the passenger behind him, and there was a sharp gasp as Bruns accidentally sank his elbow into the poor fellow's midriff.

The door lurched open with unmilitary precision, passengers surged out into the hallway, and Bruns turned to apologize to his victim—and he froze. *The Director!* My heart pounded. The three of us stood stone stiff amidstream, our eyes locked, as up-bound and down-bound passengers flooded the hallway around us. There was only one hope: that he would not recognize us. But that chance exploded the instant he addressed my roommate by name.

"Mister-Bruns. . . ." It was not a question. The Director was quite sure.

Bruns stared down into those case-hardened eyes and did his best to echo the Director's gatling delivery. "That-is-correct-sir."

The Director fired again. "Do-you-have-any-problems-as-a-new-agent-Mister-Bruns?"

"No-sir."

"How - do - you - get - along - with - your - instructors - Mister - Bruns?"

"Fine-Mister-Director."

The martial dialogue continued. A trio of fellow agents disembarked from the elevator and walked toward us, chattering and laughing as they came—until they greeted us and witnessed the panic on our faces. And then their eyes fell upon the Director and they stopped dead in their tracks, not moving for fear of falling into the line of fire. Their fear was justified. In the next instant the Director trained those hard brown eyes on me.

"What-is-your-name-sir?"

I was riveted to that bulldog's visage. Bruns had laughed at my earlier attempts at imitating the staccato delivery. I'd gotten away without it on our first meeting, so I proceeded without it. "New Agent Norman T. Ollestad, sir," I replied. And as I did his eyes shot from my clean shaven face and regulation haircut down to my glistening shoes, smoldering over the same course he had pursued with Bruns. But Keady had trained us well. I was confident. And the Director once more proved his consistency with a few standard questions.

Soon the Director ceased firing and marched slowly toward the revolving door. We followed. There was no choice in the matter: he had not dismissed us. Outside, the pedestrian traffic was congested, but somehow we arrived at the door to his limousine together. He turned to face us. Our interrogation was concluded. I looked around; our three classmates had vanished into the crowd. Only Bruns and I remained, and I prepared to take my leave. That was what the Director was waiting for. The greeting, the handshake—I would deliver them exactly as I had been instructed.

I stepped forward confidently. I reached up and set my snap-brim upon my head. And the world went black! *The hat.* Somehow my entire head had been suddenly and incredibly swallowed up in the midnight of that hat which was not my hat and which obviously belonged to someone with a head the size of a Texas watermelon.

For an eternal instant I was headless. The Director stood there motionless, speechless, most certainly trying to comprehend what was happening. First an elbow in the stomach and then a headless clown. It must have been too much for him; it *was* too much for me! All I could see was that dark blue tie and the JEH on the tie clasp and his hands. *Strong* hands. Not the trembling old man's hands of a man beyond his seventieth year. These were the powerful instruments of supreme confidence.

I wrenched myself free. He stared. "Must have walked off with the wrong hat," I mumbled.

He still stared. What would he say? What *could* he say? It was just an accident . . . but I'd heard the stories of the grim consequences to other accidents. A new agent was fired for having too many pimples. Another rode with the Director in the same elevator wearing a scarlet vest and suffered the same fate.

I practically fell over when he finally spoke. "Do-you-have-any-problems-Mister-Ollestad?"

"N-no, sir," I stammered.

"How - do - you - get - along - with - your - instructors - Mister-Ollestad?"

"Fine, sir," I replied mechanically. But I had suddenly realized he was pursuing the same pattern of questioning as he had only moments before inside the Justice building. Indeed, the Director's consistency was overwhelming.

His hard eyes fell to the hat, which was now clutched nervously in my left hand, and then shot full into my own eyes for a final brief encounter. "Well-sir," he barked, "that-hat . . . it's-too-large-for-you!" He wheeled around and slipped into the rear of the limousine, and the limousine shot out into the traffic like some dark projectile. We watched until it had vanished.

Bruns had a date that night and he grabbed the first bus home, while I went back to the Justice building to try and find my hat. Luck was with me. It was right where I'd left it.

On my way out I stopped by the men's room. I was just soaping my hands when the door behind me sprung open. Probably one of the head-watchers, I thought. I glanced up into the mirror. To my utter amazement it was Sam, the Director's receptionist.

The chunky Negro moved slowly and stiffly across to the mirror, giving no sign that he'd even noticed me. Humming softly, he pulled a small plastic brush from his pocket and applied it with surprising vigor to his coarsely upholstered scalp. It was impossible to judge how old he was, but I noticed he too had a cleverly concealed bald spot. He caught me staring. I looked away quickly.

"You're one of Mister Keady's boys, aren't you?" His bright eyes smiled into the mirror. He was still exercising that bald spot.

"That's right, Sam, I'm Norman Ollestad. I didn't think you'd recognize me." Smiling, I reached for a towel, relieved at being able to avoid the awkward problem of shaking hands. After Keady's words on the subject I wasn't sure what I should do, or for that matter what Sam expected of me.

Replacing the brush in his pocket, the Negro rinsed his hands, then turned to me. He spoke softly. "Son, I can recall the face of every man who's come through New Agents' Training for the last twenty years . . . and I ain't about to start forgetting now."

I hadn't meant to offend him. Quite the contrary. I was still embarrassed about our administrator's behavior toward him the day before, in our Director's outer office, and I wanted to be friendly.

But in a moment Sam was humming again. His eyes sparkled as he spoke. "A couple of weeks and you fellahs will be out in the field. Bet you're plenty excited about that. Then's when everything you were told here will start makin' sense. . . ."

"Like what, Sam?" I didn't really expect a direct answer. I was only making conversation.

But Sam took me seriously. "Oh . . . like your firearms training—that might just save your life some day. An' like defensive tactics . . . an' even the little bits o' things like the discipline here at training school—they'll all pay off. You watch and see."

"Are they still going to be watching us in the head?" I asked facetiously.

"No," Sam laughed, "you're on your own in that department, too."

Suddenly curiosity got the better of me. "Tell me, why *do* they watch us in the head? I never could figure that out."

Sam just kept on drying his hands, making no sign that he'd even heard me. When I tried to repeat the question he drew a dark pudgy finger to his lips and pointed to the door. And throwing the towel into the waste barrel he walked me out that door, down the corridor, and through the revolving door, and out into the freezing night air without a word. I wondered what he was up to. The Director's receptionist had been much friendlier than I'd expected. I wasn't quite sure what would happen if we were seen together. Sam was different all right. And I'd noticed he no longer spoke in the manner of the obsequious *darkey,* as he had with Keady. The accent was still deep south, but for the most part his English was as good as mine.

A light snow had begun to fall. We were almost to the bus stop, nearly a block away, before Sam spoke again. "You know, son, the walls of Justice got ears," he said poetically and then laughed at the sound of it. "You don't want to talk about dangerous things like that anywhere inside that building—even in the men's room."

"I didn't mean anything by that, Sam."

"Maybe you didn't, son, but you asked a darned good

question just the same. I ain't forcing you to listen, but if you want to know the truth I'll tell you. Just like I was your administrator and you was one of my students. And if you turn out to be a *torpedo*. . . ."

"A what?"

"Don't go askin' so many questions right now, son. You just listen and learn. And if you turn out to be a *torpedo*, reportin' me won't do you no good and it just might do you a lot of harm because I got the wherewithal to deny ever talking to you at all. Besides the boss don't understand *queers* at all. . . ."

"Well who does?" I said nervously.

Sam smiled and said nothing. I was beginning to wonder about him. Why was he taking the time and the risk to talk to me in the first place? Maybe he was *queer* himself. The thought set me on edge. We arrived at the bus stop. The snow had begun to fall more heavily now. In Washington, whenever it snows more than an inch everything drags to a halt. People abandon their cars, wherever they are. Taxi-drivers refuse to budge, and the buses stop running. And here I was on a dark night in the middle of a snow-storm, alone with the Director's colored receptionist, and not a bus in sight.

I glanced over at him. The snow seemed to agree with him, he was smiling at me. "No sir . . . if you want the truth of it, nobody understand *queers* . . . except other *queers!*"

He edged closer to me. I jerked away instinctively. But he laughed loudly and slapped me hard on the shoulder. It was a big joke to him. "No, sir, Mister Ollestad, I ain't one of them *queers* either. I'm just pullin' your leg a little. The truth of the matter is that the boss don't understand *queers*, but he's scared to death of them, and that's why they watch you fellahs in the head. . . ."

The whole thing sounded suspicious to me. I was getting disgusted with all the talk about homosexuals, and I was beginning to wonder if Keady hadn't been right about Sam. "Sure he's scared of them," I said suddenly. "They're social outcasts. Think of all the bad publicity if someone discovered a queer agent. Homosexuals are terrible security risks, too. They're too easy to blackmail."

Sam studied me for a long moment. "If you want the truth, Mister Ollestad, you're only part right. The big thing is that *queers* are just like some colored folk—they been fightin' all their lives. Fightin' and hidin' so much that they've just given up and they ain't got nothing to lose any-more so they aren't scared of nothin'. The boss can't mold people like that. And that's the thing that scares him most."

He glanced at me like he'd expected me to say something, but I didn't. Most of what he'd said had gone right by me. Sam grinned. "Now, son, that's why we got all these agents' rules. The boss likes everything to go like clockwork. The people do, too. The people know what to expect from the F.B.I.; they know we're on the job and that makes them feel safe. Those rules keep us looking respectable in the com-munity, and that's the most important thing to the boss. We got to act *respectable!*"

"Sure, but that doesn't mean the rules change. It's just that you'll get to know them better. Most of what I'm telling you about the rules you'll find out for yourself one day. But you see, the boss has got to have order. *His* order. . . ." Sam saw that he'd lost me, and he set about explaining.

"The first thing you got to understand is where the rules came from. Now take even simple things like the height and weight chart. The boss had a heart attack awhile back and the doctor told him he was too heavy and he gave him a little chart to go by. Now everybody's got to use that same chart."

Now the Negro's eyes clouded with a far-away look. He was reliving the past. "A long time back the boss got a taste for night club livin' and when he took to goin' out a lot the rule against night clubs disappeared from the Special Agents' Handbook." Sam looked at me without smiling. "When the boss got tired of it and stopped goin' to the clubs, the rule came back again."

I was beginning to see what Sam meant. He had no reason to lie to me. What he said made sense. But I was still puzzled. "How does the Bureau's attitude toward marriage fit in . . . the Director's a bachelor!"

"That's right." Sam was smiling again. "An', marriage is one of the most respectable things there is. The boss knows that as well as you and me. That's why prospective new agents who have been divorced haven't got a chance of getting into the Bureau. But there's a lot of people who think it's respectable to be a bachelor and the boss is one of them. You can't expect him to understand that all bachelor agents aren't married to the Bureau, like him. You and I know that bachelors will eventually get into trouble of some kind, either woman-trouble or man-trouble, but he'd never believe it because neither him nor Christman has ever had any of their own.

"The boss and Christman get their kicks out of playin' the bang-tails. Yes, sir—how they love to see horses run!"

"But that's gambling," I interrupted, "and there's a Bureau rule against that, too."

"Well, son, like I told you when we started, you got to learn to listen. When you get out there in the field you listen hard and maybe you can find that answer for yourself."

Seeing I was confused, Sam laughed and threw a pudgy arm about my shoulder. An old scarf clung loosely about his neck, smelling heavily of wet wool. The musty odor of sweat repulsed me. I pulled away quickly. Can't be seen embracing Negroes here in Washington, I thought.

"What's the matter, son?" he asked quietly.

I tried to cover up. "Just confused, Sam. That's all. I don't understand how you put up with it."

"With what? *Being black?*"

"That isn't what I meant. But now that you mention it, doesn't it bother you that you were never able to go through New Agents' Training like . . . everybody else?"

"Sometimes," he said softly. "But being Negro is a lot like being *queer,* I guess. When you get something—no matter even if it's a little something—you'd give your life just to hold on to it. I got my job as a Bureau clerk twenty years ago, just after I graduated from high school. And I was so thankful for that job that for five solid years I never missed a single day's work. Being part of the Bureau was more than just a little something. It made me a big man in my neighborhood. Anything I asked for was mine. I could have all the women I wanted, no questions asked. Because I was in the F.B.I. And when I got the offer from the Director to become his receptionist I jumped at the chance—even though some of my friends tried to tell me the Bureau was taking advantage of me. . . ."

"By giving you a better job?"

"In a way. They said I was being used to make the public think the Director wasn't prejudiced. But you see, out of more than six thousand agents of the F.B.I. only twenty-seven are Negroes. Without me, twenty-six.

"No, son, quitting wasn't the answer. I'm truly grateful to the boss for giving me this chance to overcome. If I'd quit chances are I'd have ended up a janitor somewhere . . . and right now I'd be boozing it up instead of fightin' it out like I am here. Here I am winning. Some folks can win bein' janitors and trash men. Not me. Here I'm famous. Everyone in the Bureau knows Sam. I make more money than you do and I've never been to college, and I have plenty of time for paintin' and readin' and doing most anything I please. But the most important thing of all is that I've learned to overcome hate and fear in myself. Sure, I know that some agents poke fun at me . . . and some like Mister Keady even hate me. But I've overcome my fear. They haven't. They've given up the very freedoms they were born with. I'm the one that's descended from slaves . . . but I'm free."

Sam turned to me. "You're not a religious man, are you Mister Ollestad?"

"Yes, I am, Sam. Maybe not the same way you are but. . . ."

"Well, it don't really matter none. But you see, it took this job to make me face up to life. When I was a young buck I went cryin' to my preacher once because I was getting treated pretty bad. I had to do stuff none of the other clerks did . . . only 'cause I was black. But my preacher didn't give me sympathy. He just said, 'Put off thy shoes from off thy feet, brother, for the place whereon thou standest is holy ground!'

"Now that didn't do much for me right off, Mister Ollestad. But when I went to work for the boss and I saw for myself how scared everybody was I started understanding what it was my preacher meant. Even when some of those southern boys came in callin' me nigger and walking all over me I could understand. An' today I'm a happy man 'cause this ground *is* holy ground; I've made my place in the Director's office holy ground. And I'm just like the great American eagle, soaring high above the storm with one eye on the sun. I've got my eye on God.

"And you know, son, I've been able to help other folks here, too. Like those southern boys. . . . I've kept a good many of them from gettin' fired, only they'll never know it. An' I've been able to talk to some boys like you'self, son. . . ."

"Why, Sam? Why take the chance? Some day you're going to tell somebody things he doesn't want to hear and everything you've worked for for the last twenty years will blow up in your face."

Sam pulled the wool muffler up around his neck and thrust his hands deep into his coat pockets. "I didn't mean no harm, son. You're the one who was askin' the questions. I just told you the truth the way I know it in my heart. I like to help folks . . . and the ones I kept from gettin' fired was all good boys. The Bureau needs them, son, just like the Bureau needs you."

Sam stared off into the distance for a long time without speaking. The snow had stopped and every now and then a car passed, and it wasn't long before the bus came. We climbed aboard and made our way to the rear of the bus and Sam stood aside and I sat by the window. We rode in silence. It seemed pitch black outside, but it didn't matter. There was nothing to see.

> *"Modern day communism, in all its many ramifications, simply cannot be understood without a knowledge of communist discipline."*
>
> J. Edgar Hoover, *Master of Deceit*

# 16

A few days before we graduated from training school, we got our field office assignments. I was assigned to Miami, Florida. The other new agents were spread throughout the United States. This news put most of the New Agents' Class in a frenzy about the government regulations applicable to the moving of their families and furniture from their home towns to their new locations. It's all they could think about, night and day. They couldn't even make conversation in the hall between class sessions without talking about how much per diem they would get traveling from the Seat of Government to their new field office assignments, and how many days they could take to move without using any of their annual leave.

We had an entire day's lecture on how to fill out the necessary forms for reimbursement of our traveling expenses, and how to use a GTR, government travel request.

The clerk who lectured us was an expert in his field, a G-18, class eighteen government employee, an indispensable advisor on the paper forms that can strangle or strengthen a government bureau. He seemed small in spite of his height of over six feet. His Adam's apple kept jumping up and down his skinny neck as he spoke, and a clean shave would be needed to cut off the straggly hairs that cropped up in little spots under his sharp chin. He wore the same garb as the instructors, very thin clip-on tie and loose trousers. But, as a Bureau clerk, he was without a coat, and wore a short-sleeved shirt, even on a bitter winter day. His manner of speaking showed the contentment of a small mind securely anchored within the confines of a few government forms. He had spent the last nineteen years with these forms and their predecessors, and the Director never made a move in the Bureau without consulting him.

I didn't share his contentment, or the interest of most of the class; probably because I was single and I had zero furniture. They all impressed me as a bunch of pettifoggers. I wanted some action. Everyone with any Bureau experience told me that the field offices would be different, there wouldn't be such a preoccupation with forms and rules, dogma. It was logical. The Seat of Government was for instruction and guidelines, the field was for execution of the principles.

I could feel the difference the moment I walked into the F.B.I. field office, on Biscayne Boulevard in Miami, Florida. Everyone looked frantically busy, but as I went through the large main office on the second floor of the building, I noticed that no agent looked up from his work without a smile and some form of friendly greeting.

I reported to a supervisor, Special Agent T. A. Fife, a somewhat rotund, but smiling and seemingly intelligent man.

"Well, Mr. Ollestad, I'm glad to see you. We need more agents here in Miami, our case load is way up this year. Our

SAC has been pleading with the Seat of Government to give us more men to help carry the load and I'm glad to see that we got you from the New Agent's Class. But we requested four agents, and this means we'll all have to work a little harder. I'm going to send you out with one of our top agents so you can get your feet on the ground, because as the Director says, 'The best way to teach or preach is by example.' Go downstairs, fill out your number three location card the same as Wilson Murray's. You'll be with him the next few days."

Murray looked like the instructors back in Washington, talked like them, too. After he supplied me with a wooden work box, a closet locker, a desk, and keys to match, he set about breaking me in. "Now, Mr. Ollestad, the first thing we have to do today is to find you a place to live, an approved place to live."

"But, Mr. Murray," I protested, "I have already filled out my number three card like yours which shows all those leads that we are going to check out." I hoped that we would see some action on my very first day out in the field, and covering the investigations listed on Murray's card might lead to something interesting. I wanted to postpone the apartment hunting. Murray responded with a condescending frown. "If we covered all those leads today, what would we have to do tomorrow?"

I forced a smile.

So Wilson Murray and I settled into a routine my first week out in the field. We went out apartment hunting like newlyweds every day, instead of fighting crime and making some arrests like I hoped we would. And each day our travels were interrupted by a two-hour service club luncheon. Murray dragged me to four of them that week. The first day we wasted two hours eating and talking with the stalwarts of the Miami Junior Chamber of Commerce. I was struck by the advanced age of the membership—if this was the *Junior* Chamber, I'd hate to see the walking cadavers that must have made up the *Senior* Chamber of Commerce.

And as I attended a few more such luncheons on subsequent days, I became aware of a certain sameness about the men and the meetings, whether it be the Optimists, the Loyal Order of Moose, or the American Legion. Each noon day I was confronted by senility and corpulence marching hand in hand, organized to do good and fight community evils such as crime and communism. All the meetings which followed lunch had a standard cast of characters—a harried, overworked president who looked upon his service as a stepping stone to greater glory—or at least an increase in his business or profession; at least one loud, righteously indignant member who was a number one commie fighter for the group; and a prankster, usually a past president, who always made a point of interrupting the business part of the meeting with what were usually some pretty funny jokes. There were also some solemn faced steady Eddies who collected fines (mostly from the prankster) and kept minutes of the meeting. Toward the end of the week, I prided myself that I could pick out the types *before* all the pre-lunch cocktails had been consumed.

Wilson Murray and I were crime and communism fighters by occupation, so we were really "in," and everyone was pleasant enough, but I was dogged by a feeling that Murray and I weren't accomplishing anything. But the older agent made the most of those luncheons. He talked and talked about the F.B.I.'s—and his—fight against evil, and half jokingly flashed his credentials around a little. If we had spent half the time out working we might have helped make a dent in the crime rate. But it was easier to talk about it in an air conditioned dining room than to go out and investigate—it was hot and sweaty out in the field.

And Murray found his level with the Moose, etc. I think he felt that without membership in all the clubs he wouldn't have had any friends—any worthwhile friends at least. When he found himself away from the friendly confines of one of the clubs he surrounded himself with an armor of shibboleths —rings, badges and jeweled pins. He was all battened down. A lion's head tie clasp kept his tie from going awry, cuff links tightened down his white sleeves. He wore a college ring on his right hand to set him apart from the uneducated, and a Masonic ring on the same hand protected him spiritually. On the third finger of his left hand Murray wore a wedding band as a shield against any designing women he might interview in the course of his work. I noticed that he changed the badge on his left lapel every day, always sporting the button of the organization we were visiting. Murray had a variety of organ- izational caps adorned with badges of accomplishment and community service. He kept them in better condition than his pistol. Against the dull suits he wore, he was always all sparkles and flashes.

"It's all true what they told you in training school, Mr. Ollestad," Murray said as we made the rounds. "The Bureau doesn't rush into things. As the Director always says, 'Take care of the little things, they are important, and the big things will take care of themselves.' And nothing is more important than the neighborhood and atmosphere in which an agent lives, especially a young single agent. That's why we want you to live in Bureau approved housing. If you were to get into some kind of trouble living in an unapproved area, Fife and I would hang for it. We in the F.B.I. always proceed at a normal pace, build slowly, but with strength. Take bank robberies for instance. The local police rush out to the scene with furious activity, but if they don't catch the suspects at the scene, they've had it, and they usually give up. We in the F.B.I. take our time with each robbery and systematically work the case until we eventually apprehend the thieves."

That's what Murray told me that first week out in the field as we drove around town looking for my apartment. He let on as if he was the big bank robbery man in the Miami field office, but I found out afterwards that Murray took all the credit for the work of one of the agents who worked under him.

On Friday of my first week, Murray and I returned to the office promptly at 5:00 P.M., but I didn't want to leave. I was still excited about my new assignment.

"Better check out, Ollestad, you don't want to run the voluntary overtime of the office up above the average for the month, do you?"

I looked to see if Murray was joking. He was laughing, but the tone of his voice made him serious. We both walked over to the number one register and signed out for the night and Murray took off for home like a shot. I stayed in the office. As I nosed from desk to desk in the main office, everyone went out of his way to ignore me, refused to speak. My friendly questions brought only grunts. There were no smiles. Within the space of one working week, I'd done something wrong. I walked over to the corner of the room where an agent was listening to Radio Havana. I tried again. "Hi," I grinned.

The agent motioned me into a chair by the receiver. "Castro, do you understand it?" he asked.

"No, it's too Cuban, too fast."

Only the fanatical voice of the radio was heard for the next half hour. I lost the trend of the speech almost immediately, but didn't move. I had a chance to study my only apparent friend. The agent was deeply tanned, rather thin, with worn out blue eyes. He wore a wide striped tie. Coat off and hanging on the back of his chair, the sleeves of his blue button-down shirt were rolled up to his elbows, showing powerful rippling forearms. His face was lined, but too kindly, too easy, to make him formidable. He was not to be feared. His sunken cheeks contrasted sharply with Fife's fat puffy ones. He looked like he didn't enjoy good restaurants, or good drink, like my supervisor.

The broadcast ended with some military music. "I'm S. A. Walton E. Post." He extended a powerful hand. "That was Fidel."

"I'm Norman Ollestad, from the New Agents' Class."

"So I've heard. Went around with Murray this week, huh?"

"Yes."

"Notice that your reception was a little different from your first morning?"

"I thought it was my imagination."

"I don't know whether or not you're a torpedo, but we all may find out now."

"What's the problem?" I asked.

"The way you signed in on the number one register this week. You know what I mean?"

"No. I thought I filled it in the way it says in the agent's handbook. I had made a special point of doing it right. What the hell is wrong with you guys?" I protested.

Post smiled at me. "You've got to sign the register two minutes after the time listed in the space above your name, regardless of what time it is when you sign in. Like today, you signed in at 7:48, but the agent who signed in just before you put down 6:45, so you should have put in 6:47."

"Are you kidding? I don't like the idea of cheating on the time sheet. That's a technical violation of the False Statement to the Government Statute," I informed him.

"It's the only way we can get in the required amount of overtime without staying here every night."

"Is there a required amout of overtime?" I asked. "I thought that it was something that couldn't be helped. In fact, I remember reading the Director's report to Congress. He says our overtime is administratively uncontrollable, it crops up occasionally from the nature of the work."

"Make it easy on yourself and listen, Ollestad. This overtime is very tricky. You'll be in trouble if you have either more or less than the office average. Last month the average 'administratively uncontrollable' overtime was 3 hours and 20 minutes per day, and if you were above or below that average by fifteen minutes, you were in trouble."

"How?"

"It meant you were not pulling your share of the load if you were under, and that you were not efficient enough if you were over."

"What if you had more work to do than the average?"

"All Bureau agents have the same amount of work, there is no favoritism shown here. Each agent can do the job of any other agent and . . ." Post broke out into a broad grin, he was on the verge of a hearty laugh. "You'll learn. You're smart enough to catch on. I really didn't have to stick my neck out and tell you to cheat on the number one register, but the rest of us would have had to suffer for the month or so that it took you to figure it out, so I offered myself as a sacrifice for the good of the rest of these lunkheads and took a chance that you were not a torpedo."

"What's a torpedo?"

"An agent that spies on other agents. You can't see him until it's too late . . . just like a torpedo. A torpedo works either for the Director, supervisors, or the SAC—does unspeakable things, all in the name of his wife and children."

"I don't follow."

"A torpedo's justification is that he has a wife and kids to support and so cannot run the risk, like the rest of us, of getting fired. He plays it safe. You'll learn as you go along. The first thing to do is to forget everything they taught you in training school, become a good agent like a few of the guys here, and you won't have to worry about all this petty stuff. There is a lot to do, not enough agents who want to work. Instead of going around with Murray get out with Spence. You might learn how to work a case."

"Okay." I figured I couldn't do any worse than Murray. "What do you do besides give advice to new agents?" I joked.

"I'm on the security squad. I have five of Castro's finest agents all to myself. I've turned two of them. If you think your Spanish is good enough, when you get settled, I'll take you along to see a real live intelligence agent."

"Thanks, see you tomorrow." I wanted to talk some more, but I could see from the mountain of reports on his desk that Post was busy. Without knowing for sure, I felt that Walton Post was the type of agent that I would eventually like to be, the kind that actually did things in the Bureau. Wally's job seemed so interesting, that you'd almost do it for no pay at all. I found out later that S. A. Walton Post

felt the same way, and that's why the rules of personal conduct and office procedures didn't get him down. It was the
sacrifice he made to be able to work at an occupation he enjoyed. And he did important work.

I walked over to my locker, slowly took off my gun belt,
unhitched my brand new revolver, locked it up, and left the
office. It was hot and damp outside. I had absolutely nothing
to do, so I thought I'd walk back to the hotel.

"Hey, Ollestad. Where you going?" I turned around. It
was Wally. "I just got a call from the Cubano agent of mine."
He walked up to me. "You've got an innocent face, want to
come along?"

We both got into Wally's battered Buick and started for
the old Negro section of Miami, recently occupied by the
Cubans.

"Aren't we going to get a Bureau car?" I wanted to know.

"No, we might have to go on a surveillance and with no
other cars working I won't need the radio."

"Why use your own car? It's F.B.I. business."

"You haven't been keeping up on the Bureau rules. If I
get into an auto accident while on a surveillance or any other
time, I'll be fired if the accident is determined to be my fault.
Each accident calls for an immediate and full field investigation by the auto squad, and they would be mad as hell to
have to get up at this time of night and investigate *my* problem. Besides, I would have to pay for all the damage to the
Bu car out of my own pocket."

"Aren't they insured?"

"No, each agent has to carry his own insurance on the Bu
cars."

"Do you ever use a government auto?"

"Sure, I have to, but I don't like to use them for a 'tail' unless there is more than one car working with radio contact because I can't follow close enough—I might get into an accident if I take too many chances. Here's some more advice for you Ollestad. When you check out a Bureau car, always take the oldest one in the bunch. If you bend a fender or something it'll cost you a lot less."

From the tone of his voice and facial expression, I could tell that these little things didn't bother Wally a bit. In fact he seemed amused by it all. Apparently, as long as he could work his Cuban agents and collect intelligence, he didn't mind using his own auto. He was the closest thing to a happy man I'd ever met.

"Let me tell you a little about the agents Castro sends over here. They sleep all day, carouse all night. They don't let a little intelligence work stand in the way of their women, although it does curtail their drinking. The Bureau office hours are eight-fifteen to five, but they don't operate under those restrictions. Just try to keep up with them every night. It's nasty if you like sleep." He chuckled and made a sharp turn, then an immediate stop right in front of the Cubana Club. If we were supposed to make a secret entry the screech of the Buick's brakes ruined it. But, apparently this wasn't the idea.

The Cubana Club had it all, music roaring into the dark sticky night, the smell of stewed chicken, rice, rancid butter, and every Cuban in Miami. We entered the crowded bar portion of the small whitewashed building. It smelled of sweat and cheap perfume. We were immediately greeted by a young Cuban girl, very pretty face, jet black hair, nice figure—until she walked away from the bar and revealed tremendous hips so fat they were pushing out in lumps from the sides of her tight dress.

"He's home," she said in perfect American.

We shouldered our way outside without another word.

"Aren't you worried about the girl, she recognized you so obviously," I warned Wally.

"No, it's a typical confused Cuban arrangement. They all think Phil has turned me and I've given him some worthless information along with $500 a month in American dollah that he can pass along. But he's worth his weight in gold to me. I've made every agent Castro has sent over here for the last 6 months and an ident on the guy that hijacked that commercial airplane and took it to Havana."

"What good is an identification if he and the plane are in Havana?"

"We can usually get an indictment returned against him by the grand jury here in Miami, and when he returns to the U. S. or its possessions we can apprehend him. It gets the Director off the hook, and us too, once we get that identification, then it's a State Department problem."

"Where do you get the $500 to pay this informant?"

"The Bureau pays its informants in hard cash, but the rule is that you never give out the money without getting a receipt."

He was joking. I noticed later when the Cuban agent was paid off, Walton didn't bother about a receipt.

The Buick stopped in front of an unpainted, unlit shack. I expected to see an old Negro sitting on the front porch smoking a pipe, but instead caught a black Cuban emerging from the shadows at the side of the house. He walked up to the car and got in the front seat beside me. I watched in vain for some secret sign or signal; so far nothing much had happened on this assignment.

Walton spoke in English. "What do you have for me to-night, you old bastard?"

"Nada. . . ." And then, the black man spoke so rapidly in Cuban that I lost him.

Post laughed, fished a fistful of twenty dollar bills from his shirt pocket, and threw them across the front seat. They were snatched out of the air right in front of my face by a black hand with fingers so yellowed by smoke and nicotine, that it was noticeable in the dashboard lighting inside the car. His name was Phil, this Cuban agent. He had God damned long fingernails and smelled just like the Cubana night club, a strong odor of chicken, rice and butter. He was quieter, but what a greaser. He was dressed in bell bottomed trousers and an ancient starched white dress shirt unbuttoned almost all the way down the front. Castro is in trouble sending these clods over to the U. S., I thought. No wonder we turn so many of them. It's a good thing Walton speaks his language. I looked at the Cuban out of the corner of my eye. Phil looked straight ahead, bleary eyed and silent.

We drove for more than five minutes without a word. I was impatient, I wanted to exchange some information. At least they could have gotten out some maps and pin-pointed Castro's troop concentrations, or located some missiles. But they didn't seem interested.

Finally, I decided to help Wally out. "Where are we going?" I asked.

"El Pollo Gordo, Phil?" Wally asked.

"Sss. . . ." Phil hissed in Spanish.

"Jesus! He can't even speak Spanish," I thought.

"How is your brother, Phil?" Wally said.

The black man answered in perfect American. "My brother is in excellent health."

My head jerked around in surprise, then I accentuated my error by immediately jerking it back. As I stared straight ahead, I was glad the darkness hid my red ears.

The Cuban continued. "There is no chance, save your money, do you want a check-up for next Wednesday?"

"What's wrong, don't you like the Yankee cash I give you?" Post asked him.

"I would like to please you, but I cannot. All the farmers love Fidel, including me. We would all fight for him to-morrow, if called upon. Especially against you fat Yankee pigs."

Walton's white teeth showed he was grinning. "I'll see you in one week, unless you call me."

"Okay, boss," Phil answered. "They didn't send the man tonight like I thought they would. Sorry."

The Buick stopped a block away from another night club. Phil jumped out. As we pulled away, I watched him bend over counting the money under a street light.

"Up until now he has given me hard information," Wally explained to me. "And he says the CIA is receiving an erro-neous impression from their informants about Fidel's grass root strength. In Cuba, the Bureau has better intelligence. At least before our agents got kicked out we did. We still seem to have better informants here in the U.S. Our boys indicate that an invasion force in the next year has absolutely no chance of support internally. He was quiet tonight, but he usually tries to pump me for information because he sells to the other side too."

"I thought he was a Cuban government agent, isn't he supposed to work for nothing?" I asked.

"Yes, but once those Cubans get over here, most of them try for some extra money by milking their own government.

. . . Remember when you work security never give out more information than you receive. Some agents just can't work this squad, because they have a knack for giving out all their aces to obtain only a little information in return."

That evening was one of the biggest disappointments of my Bureau career. Although I didn't let on to Wally, who had been nice enough to take me along, security work was not for me . . . at least Cuban security work. From what Wally told me, and from what I saw, nothing was ever accomplished, you were forever spinning wheels. Post never apprehended any of the Cuban agents he discovered, he just kept tabs on them, and tried to turn them. His big thrill was "turning" a double agent, but even then there was no completion, no finality to the case. As he explained it, if he arrested one of Castro's agents as soon as he identified him and caught him violating the espionage statute or some other federal law, Cuba would immediately send over another one, and the fellows on the Cuban security squad would have to start all over again attempting to find him. So they kept all their own Cuban agents to themselves, kept them out of harm's way, and merely watched, and reported what they did.

The night Wally had me handle one of his assignments alone didn't change my opinion of Cuban intelligence either. The second week in the Miami office I received a phone call from Wally at 3 A.M.

"Do you like your work, Mr. Ollestad," he asked.

"Yeah," I answered sleepily. I wasn't sure who was calling.

"You like the idea of being a special agent of the F.B.I., eh?"

I was a little more awake at this time and recognized Post's voice as I answered, "Yes, sir."

"This is Wally. I have a conflict with two of my informants

—I can't be in two parts of Miami at the same time—do you think you could help me out? This is just routine, you'll only be a delivery boy."

"Yeah, Wally, I'd be glad to."

I strapped on my trousers and my gun belt, fumbled with a shirt and tie, and waited out in front of Mike Gordon's restaurant near the Miami Beach causeway where Wally was to pick me up. The plan was for Wally to leave me off at the Cubana Club where Phil was to meet me, pick me up in his own automobile, exchange information—the name of a Castro agent newly arrived from Cuba—and the usual $500. Then Phil was to drop me off in front of Mike Gordon's restaurant. By the time we reached the Cuban night club I was wide awake. The music inside was as loud as ever, but I had trouble finding the girl who usually worked behind the bar. I looked around in vain, went over and stood by the doorway. After a few minutes I felt a girl's hand placed on the back of my neck. I turned around and it was the young Cuban girl with the grotesquely enormous hips. She spoke little English, so I struggled through in Spanish and tried to explain that I was looking for Phil. It was impossible to hear her with all the noise inside, so we walked out on the sidewalk, and then she told me that Phil was not going to be there tonight and that she was to take his place in the same way as I was taking Wally's place. From that moment I sensed that my mission would be a failure. She led me to an alley at the rear of the club where an old Chevrolet was parked. After about ten minutes of standing beside the car, I finally understood her Cuban dialect enough to realize that she couldn't drive, so I opened the passenger door, let her in and jumped behind the wheel myself. A half hour later we were still sitting there. I couldn't start the car for the life of me. I tried every method in the world, pumping the gas, pressing the starter without touching the accelerator. I even tried to push the car, but it wouldn't roll in the rock-strewn alley. To this day I think that Chevrolet was out of gas. Finally, I threw up my hands and tried to explain in very slow and meticulous Castilian Spanish to an uncomprehending young Cuban girl that I had given up that part of the plan which called for us to drive me back to Mike Gordon's restaurant, and I requested the name of the agent. At first I got no response, then I flashed the $500 in small bills, and I got ten names—everything from Che Guevara to Juan Marichal.

After a round or two of the name game, I lost patience and made a motion to leave. She put her arm around my shoulder and finally settled on one name. Wally told me later that it was the correct one. Apparently she had given me the other names to stall for time; she didn't seem to want to leave. I offered her the $500 pay off. She pushed the money back at me and put her other arm around my shoulders. She whispered that her name was Maria something, and in halting English said we should see more of each other. We sat there in the darkness for awhile, neither of us saying a word, while Maria nuzzled against my chest and puckered her lips at me. I'd still probably be sitting in the car with Maria trying to figure out what to do, but after twenty minutes of silent sparring, Maria dug her fingernails into the back of my neck and hung a giant, wet kiss on the corner of my mouth. The kiss wasn't that bad, but the jab at my neck spurred me to action. I leaped out of the Chevrolet with the money in hand and ran all the way across town to the spot where Wally Post was to pick me up again.

I didn't do too much Cuban security work alone after my

bout with Maria, but following Wally Post around gave me an insight into the plight of the Cuban people since Fidel Castro's rise to power.

It seemed that both the FBI and the Central Intelligence Agency were, because of differing responsibilities, furiously compiling all the intelligence on Castro's Cuba they could get their hands on. Around Miami, the FBI's security squad (with Wally Post doing most of the work) was concerned about the threat to the internal security of the United States posed by the Castro agents. The Central Intelligence Agency concentrated on the situation in Cuba itself, and from what we heard, was trying to remedy the situation there. Both the FBI and the CIA used spies who were called "informants," but for some inexplicable reason, neither agency used the same "informants." I quickly learned that our spies were better—at least more honest. As Wally told it, the FBI "informants" hired by the Miami agents gave us the true information, bitter or sweet as it might be. Through the FBI's Cuban spies we also learned what kind of intelligence the CIA was receiving, and it seemed that the CIA's spies were coloring their facts with distortions designed to please and encourage the Central Intelligence Agency. The thrust of Fidel Castro's internal strength, and its extent, was pointedly withheld from the CIA so as not to discourage them from a planned invasion of Cuba.

One of the crucial problems was trying to assess the inarticulate, quixotic Cuban peasants and the others still left in Cuba in order to determine if they would support Castro or the Cuban freedom government in the event of an invasion of Cuba by the exiles.

One of Wally's "double agents," Doctor Jaime Effimenco, gave us an insight. The doctor was slightly plump, and a very warm, well educated man. But he was so introspective and reticent that until I had gotten to know him (by tagging along with Wally) it amazed me that he could be a spy—he seemed at first like a typical quiet scientific type who just minded his own business and was too meek to go looking for trouble.

Doctor Effimenco had been a wealthy man in Cuba, but had helped Fidel Castro's rise to power because he hated Castro's predecessor, Dictator Fulgencio Batista. The doctor had been sent to Miami by the Castro government to collect information—to spy, but in less than six months Wally, with the help of Fidel's blunderings back in Cuba, turned the doctor—made him a double agent—an agent of the United States as well as Cuba. Doctor Effimenco played a violin in a Miami restaurant (he was not allowed to practice medicine in the United States), posed as Castro's agent, and regularly supplied information to the FBI. But it wasn't the money that had turned him, even though the doctor was hard pressed to sustain his family who had accompanied him to the United States. What had caused the doctor to spy on his own country, and to sell to the United States, was a sort of half defeated hope that the United States could win his country back and give the Cuban people another chance at a democracy.

Many times while we waited for Wally to finish the rough notes for a report, Doctor Effimenco would tell me about Cuba and her people. I learned that the peasants left back in Cuba composing a large segment of Castro's army were simple, hard, and long suffering, and expected nothing more out of life than to be allowed to work at labor every day except Sundays for the rest of their lives. As a group they were inarticulate, and most were illiterate. Their concept of communism was limited to a rather utopian ideal of "social justice" in which it would be possible for their children to have all the opportunities open to the rich man's families. It was kept from them that communism would ultimately be a threat to their religion. The simple people were excited about seeing Fidel Castro playing baseball with them, and giving away land to the small farmers, and Castro was nurturing a fledgling sense of nationalism in them.

On the other hand, the leaders of the freedom movement —Cubans who had been wealthy and educated enough to flee Cuba in the very beginning of Castro's regime—were not getting through to the people left in Cuba. By their very nature, the elite that had fled Castro were ill equipped to liberate their own country. Most of the members of the Cuban liberation movement, from the leaders down to the rank and file, were born and raised under the aegis of a dictator, and by the very reason of their success had to tacitly or overtly cooperate with and support the dictatorship. Most of the Cubans for Freedom located in the United States were very articulate, some in both English and Spanish. They could move one almost to tears, speaking of individualism and liberty at the big freedom rallies and on the radio broadcasts in Miami and New York. The words came easy to the Freedom Cubans just as it was difficult for the Cubans back on the island to express themselves at all. Perhaps for this very reason, the Cubans still on the island distrusted words —and were suspicious of the speeches of the exiles—they didn't fully appreciate the grandiose oratory coming from the exiles' outposts in the United States. The Freedom Cubans were associated in the minds of the peasants with Batista, a dictator who didn't even play baseball with them, didn't give any land away, and failed to even give any lip service to the concept of "social justice." It was plain to Doctor Effimenco that the Cuban peasant would never fight against Castro to re-establish people with the taint of Batista on them.

But it was far from clear to the CIA. Looking at Cuba, they could see that the country, under Castro, was going from bad to worse. Havana, the main city, was radically different than it had been under Fulgencio Batista—not as much easy tourist money now, and some of those in the city couldn't get all the toilet articles and appliances that they were used to. The large land holdings were being broken up by the government—the Castro family was one of the first to liquidate their extensive rancheros—and were being distrib-uted to the peasants in small farms to work on their own. This worsened the economic crisis because without high mechanization, which Cuba lacked, the type of crops grown in Cuba—sugar cane, tobacco, etc.—are economically pro-duced only by large plantations. As a result of the dissolution of the large land holdings, the production of Cuba's cash crops was falling off critically.

To the Central Intelligence Agency—looking at Cuba through its informants—it seemed impossible that the Cubans still left in their homeland could be impressed by the fanat-ical ravings of Fidel Castro, and his foolish grandstand plays which were ruining the country's economy. It was logical to the Central Intelligence Agency that there would be wide-spread unrest in Cuba, and disenchantment among the people as the economic squeeze progressed. If any of the campesinos back in Cuba had been educated enough, or perceptive enough to see what was really happening to their nation, there might have really been a climate ripe for an anti-Castro revolution, but such an atmosphere existed only in the high hopes and wishful thinking of the CIA. The peasants would support Fidel.

Doctor Effimenco knew this, and he felt that the Cubans for Freedom—and he was by blood and station one of them—could not recapture Cuba by themselves, and alone establish a democracy devoted to individual freedom, because they had absolutely no experience in democracy or individual freedom. All they really knew was a totalitarian form of government.

"It's very extraordinary that our leaders can even expound on theoretical democracy," the doctor told us several times. "It's a step forward, I think," he would always add. The doctor was candid in his introspective appraisals of himself and his fellow Cuban exiles. "If you recapture our Cuba back for us, we *can* establish a democracy there, most probably. But indeed," he told us, "you'll have to get our country back for us, we can't do it alone. Too soft, too soft, the white collar workers and men of professions that are exiled here in the United States. Hand to hand, we can't defeat the peasants. We can outtalk them, but not outfight them."

"Please, Doctor," Wally always cut in. Wally felt that high minded political discussions cut off the supply of factual and useful information which he needed more than theories. "Don't underestimate yourselves, Doctor, you're the cream of the crop, here in the United States," Wally would assure him.

"With the mind yes, but not fighting," the doctor persisted.

After each interview or freedom rally when the doctor wasn't around, Wally would always give me the benefit of a summary. "We're not concerned with the freedom movement except as it affects the security of the United States—

we in the FBI have to keep close watch on the Cuban agents because of espionage. It's the CIA that has to worry about the probabilities of success of an anti-Castro invasion and overthrow. As things look now they'll never make it unless they get the U.S. Marines to go in there and take over for them."

"That's what they'll do huh?" I asked.

"How do I know? It hasn't anything to do with me, with the FBI. As a matter of fact, we've offered our information to the CIA boys, but they're not too interested. Seems that they think we're a bunch of hicks, me and the rest of the FBI Cuban security squad. They're kind of ivy league types, the CIA agents I've met. They kind of sneer at me—good naturedly—they joke about it but they can't hide it—they sneer. I guess they've heard about all the bureaucratic red tape our squad gets bogged down in or some of the war stories about how we have to spend our time bowing and scraping to the Director or to a supervisor—" Wally looked at me intently, then good naturedly punched me in the ribs and sighed. "In spite of it all, we're doing so much better than those egg heads—it's a feeling of competition between the two agencies—can't escape it—and by God, the FBI is beating the pants off the hot shots at Cuban Intelligence."

From what I'd heard it was because Walton Post and most of his Cuban security fellow agents went far beyond the call —I guess their pride did it for them.

I was sure that my sense of self esteem would carry me through too. But I had to start learning how to work a case on my own. Wally kept telling me to try to get out with the Georgia Cracker I. A. Spence, and I eventually had the opportunity.

# 17

It wasn't easy. The Georgia Cracker didn't like young punk agents tagging along with him. I followed him from the field office out to the garage one morning and waited for him to choose a Bureau car, then I tried to get his permission to go along.

"Mr. Spence, I'm Norman Ollestad, from the New Agents' Class. It's been suggested that I go out with you today." I tried to leave the impression that Fife had recommended it.

Special Agent I. A. Spence scowled at me, "You tell that supervisor to mind his own affairs and quit preying on his brothers." He brushed me aside and walked toward the car.

"But Agent Post said you would teach me how to work a case." I had begged a little, and that made it worse. Spence was in the car by this time and about ready to drive off.

"Look, Mr. Spence, I just got out of training school, and I've spent my entire Bureau career in the field looking for an apartment. I want to start doing something."

It worked. He sat looking straight ahead for a moment, then motioned for me to get into the car.

"Now first thing you do, boy, is to forget all that foolishness they taught you back in training school." He spoke slowly with a thick tongue.

He didn't use any of the right words, the Bureau words. I wondered how he managed to dictate his Bureau reports. I noticed an irregular band of sweat stain around the crown of the hat he wore. I saw that he favored flowered ties, and his pocked complexion made him look unwashed. How could this man have survived in our Bureau for over fifteen years, I thought. Wally had told me the torpedos covered for him; and the brass, the SAC and ASAC and his supervisor Murray, protected him during the inspections. I found out later that it was because he obtained such miraculous results in bank robbery cases. He solved all of them. Nothing irked the Director more than unsolved bank robberies since bankers are usually the leading citizens of any community and the Bureau needed their active support. The Cracker kept the pressure off the Miami Office.

We drove north on Highway One. "Now the second thing to remember, boy, is not to shake hands with any niggers while the local PD's are watching you. You may be from the west but you're in the south now, and the local police don't like that sort of thing. We need their cooperation to solve these bank robberies."

I wondered how he could tell I was from California. Maybe my speech. Well, there was no doubt about his origin. I was disappointed; after the buildup Wally gave him, I had hoped Spence would be something special. All I'd learned from him so far was a lesson in bigotry. I braced myself for another disillusioning afternoon in the field working for the F.B.I.

The Cracker and I then turned toward the northeast section of Miami and it became hot. I began to sweat through my shirt and my wash and wear suit where my back rested up against the car seat. It was springtime in Florida. My first days in Miami always began with a cool, beautiful sunrise that pumped me full of high hopes and enthusiasm. But after a warming early morning, each day seemed to settle down to a breezy but nonetheless sweltering afternoon which always sapped my energy and made it difficult to work. By the time we reached the East Miami Negro section, the blazing sun had dried up the evening dews, and dust swirled around our car as the Cracker drove off the paved highway and we rolled through the dirt streets of the neighborhood. In spite of the heat I was tempted to roll up the window on my side of the car because my sweaty hands were turning a light brown with the sticky powder thrown up by the front wheels of our auto. What if my hands were chocolate brown all the time, I thought. What if I were brown all over? I wondered if I would be riding with the Georgia Cracker in an F.B.I. automobile as a fellow agent. No, sir, not with the Cracker at least. He'd shown his racial prejudice already. I figured that he probably hated the Negroes standing on the corners, the young kids playing kick the can in the dusty street who waved at us as we passed. He hated them; and yet we were going to a Negro's home and Spence was going to ask the Negro to inform on his friends. That's how it looked to me as we arrived at the unpainted shanty occupied by Orestes White, a small house of grey boards speckled with spots of brown rust where the old nail heads showed through.

As he stopped the car and reached under the dash board to set the brake, Spence whispered some advice.

"Now, here boy, these people are dirt poor southern folks, the likes of which you've never seen in California. Don't be fooled now, the more experienced you get as an investigator, the less you're going to rely on first impressions."

Spence got out of the car and walked around to the back after locking the door on his side. "Here boy, put your revolver in the trunk and I'll lock it. It won't do to take it into Bob's house."

Bob's house. Why does he call the man by a nickname?

What's wrong with Mr. White or Orestes White, I thought. I'll bet the Cracker's incapable of calling the Negro "Mister."

"... first impressions," the Cracker repeated, "don't let them fool you. These colored folks don't usually say much but some are very sensitive, very perceptive, and if you're just fooling them or you're not for sure, they'll still smile at you all right, and say yes, sir, and no, sir, but they'll know you're a faker and they won't help you—they won't like you either. Some policemen think they can scare information out of these blacks, but a few of these niggers are stubborn as a Missouri mule. You can't do nothin' to scare 'em." The Cracker jerked his head toward the house. "This here Bob's one of them—stubborn—that's why I'm partial to him."

The Cracker caught himself, and glanced at me quickly to get my reaction. He had a guilty look, like he'd just realized that he was talking too much about things that were none of my business. So he cut short the discussion, closed the car trunk lid after I placed my Smith & Wesson inside, but then seemed to change his mind again and shot some final words of advice as we walked up to the house.

"It's heart to heart, boy; they can pick it up somehow. If your heart's not with 'em, they know it."

As we walked up three short steps to a porch constructed of grey, warped, weathered boards that looked as if they had never seen a coat of paint, I felt that the Cracker was not being honest with me. He called these people "niggers," and *he'd* been taught from birth not to even call to them by their surnames, and yet he was telling *me* to speak and act from the heart. *I* wasn't prejudiced.

The floor of the porch creaked when we walked to the front door. All of the boards weren't nailed down and they moved when I stepped on them. I noticed as I looked down at my footing that the porch had been swept clean of the dust which lay in mounds in the front yard. There were no trees, no grass, no shrubbery in Mr. White's yard. A large shiny black woman appeared at the screened front door.

"Good day," the Cracker said. "Is the man of the house in today?"

The Negro woman didn't say anything, but matter of factly opened the screen door and let us in. We had come at an inopportune time; the Whites were preparing to eat breakfast—or lunch—or whatever it was. There wasn't much light inside the house, only a few small windows graced the main room. I noticed Orestes White get up from the kitchen table in the adjoining room, wave away three young children, and walk in to greet us.

"Yes sir, yes sir," he said when he saw Spence. Orestes White wore faded, very light blue overalls over a more faded lighter blue long sleeved shirt with the collar buttoned all the way up as if to wear a tie, but he wore none—I doubt he owned one. His attire was so clean, neat, worn, and pale blue that I almost expected him to possess pale blue eyes to match. But Orestes was coal black with pearly white teeth and very dull black eyes. As I observed the Cracker and Orestes at the kitchen table while they talked and sipped coffee, the Negro impressed me as a kindly old man who ran his household the same way that the Georgia Cracker probably ran his. There didn't seem to be much place for the wife and children while we discussed "business"; the children were absent the whole time and Mr. White's wife was seen but not heard. Orestes knew all the young Negro women in the community who were engaged in prostitution, and knew where they operated. Orestes seemed to evince sort of an ambivalent attitude toward it—it seemed that it was a way these girls could economically raise themselves out of the dusty prison of East Miami nigger town, and apparently it wasn't such a disgrace after all. But it also turned out that most of the girls didn't want to change from prostitution even in those cases where the pimps didn't rob them blind and they could afford it. What knocked me for a loop was the information that most of the "tricks" turned by the girls were white men. It came out matter of factly, and the Cracker knew all about it so he didn't react that I could notice. But I wondered if the Cracker ever thought philosophically about it. Nothing seemed more terrible to the southern red necks than the possibility that some "nigger" sometime would, if given a chance, rape their white women and thereby mongrel-ize the race. But it never occurred to these men that the same result could be accomplished by carousing with Negro prostitutes. The progeny would still be half and half.

But now it was time to eat. Orestes called his wife, and she set a spoon, knife and a bowl in front of each of us seated at the table.

"It's kind of late, shouldn't we be moving on?" I hinted to Spence. I was looking for an excuse to leave before the meal. The house was spotless, the kitchen table had a bright linoleum top, and our bowls were sparkling, but food didn't look too appetizing. Everytime I looked over at the ancient grease-covered, coal black stove where the meal was being prepared, my stomach skipped a beat, and I tried to ignore the fat black hands that were frying the ham. I was going to repeat my question, but I happened to notice Spence, who was seated across the table. His jaw tightened ever so little, and a slight wave of color passed through his face. He was silent, but I knew he was furious at me. He'd taken pains to warn me. "From the heart," he'd said, and now I was making it obvious that I didn't want to pass a quiet afternoon with Orestes White, eating his food, and exchanging criminal information in return for some sociability. I wanted it to be all take and no give, and I would miss the opportunity to gain an insight which might be helpful in future criminal investigations. Maybe the Cracker was being nice to me, taking me around with him to see how he operated, and maybe this was one of his secrets. At any rate, I knew from the look on his face that I wouldn't be out with him tomorrow unless I shut up. So like the woman of the house, I was silent. I watched her set the meal in front of him and saw the set line of his mouth relax and his annoyance subsided. We ate fried ham, big slabs of it, with greens—the greens turned out to be the steamed tops of beets! I almost gagged, but I managed to get most of it down. Mrs. White also served grits—corn grits—soaked so they were white and looked just like cream of wheat cereal. I was going good on the tasteless grits, putting on a pretty good show, when disaster struck.

Mrs. White poured a few cupfuls of black coffee in the sputtering frying pan filled with ham grease, then stirred the steaming potion slowly with a large spoon.

That's a crazy way to clean out the pan, I thought warily as I scooped another spoonful of the grits.

"Ah, that's what we wait'n for," Orestes said softly, "some Red Eye gravy."

I watched the grease and the coffee congeal in the pan and thought surely that the Negro was teasing me. I saw him wink at the Cracker. He *was* teasing me. I saw the Cracker smile, and it made me feel a little better because I knew for sure that the Cracker wasn't irritated anymore. But the Red Eye gravy was forthcoming! Orestes' wife gave it a few more swirls, then picked up the frying pan with the

crusty black outside rim and carried it over to my place at
the table where she poured the Red Eye generously over
my corn grits. I watched it trickle into the beet tops and
over the ham. She did the same with the Cracker and her
husband. We all gulped it down rapidly. They ate with
relish. My stomach was still rumbling hours later.

I was a little perturbed at the Georgia Cracker. He
wouldn't go to school with niggers, wouldn't go to church
with 'em, but by God he'd come down to East Miami and
live with 'em, come right down and eat their food. I was
puzzled about it too.

After lunch, Orestes and the Cracker smoked some foul
smelling corn cob pipes and talked for almost two hours—
and not altogether about crime. Most of the time was spent
arguing about race horses; not the thoroughbred kind that I
associated with horse racing, but the trotters and pacers that
dragged a buggy, or a sulky behind them. They disagreed
about blood lines, whether or not to breed speed to speed or
speed to endurance or something like that. I lost interest in
the discussion right away and had a chance to study Orestes
and the house he lived in. The Negro didn't bow and scrape
to me because I was an FBI agent, or for any other reason.
He and the Cracker took it for granted that I didn't know
anything about horses and kept me out of the conversation.
I had the feeling that Orestes felt that I, as a youngster,
should be quiet like his wife and children. We sat in a room
with curtains but no glass in the windows; in fact, none of
Mr. White's windows were covered with anything but screens.
Every wall in the kitchen and living room was painted white;
there were no rugs on the floor.

Then it was time to leave. I was relieved. A longer stay
might mean some more refreshments. The Cracker took up

his hat and gave Orestes a friendly pat on the shoulder.

"See you directly, Bob," the Cracker said.

"Yes, *Mister* White," I added, "we'll be by again. Thank you." I extended my hand for one of the FBI's famous firm handshakes of friendship. Orestes hesitated. It was written all over his face that he was troubled; he didn't trust me. Finally, to get me to put down my arm, he reached out and sort of touched the palm of my hand—he didn't grip my hand, just barely touched it. And he forced a smile. I really liked that guy Orestes, I was all for him. I wanted him to know I was his friend, but I guess he didn't catch on.

The Cracker unlocked the Bureau car and we drove to our next interview.

# 18

I learned more that afternoon about the art of investigation than in 13 weeks back at the Seat of Government.

The old Cracker was magnificent, his observations incisive; his appraisals of people and their inner feelings and motivations were uncanny.

As we entered a bank that had been robbed a week before, Spence took off his brown, wide brimmed hat, held it in his lap, and meekly sat in the lobby, waiting to see the bank manager for permission to re-interview some of the witnesses to the robbery. While we waited, he studied the walls, ceiling, the floor. He cased the room as if he were planning to rob the bank himself.

As they began their second round of interviews, the proud, white shirted bank tellers quickly overcame the awesome F.B.I. credentials Spence showed them, and regained their initial feeling of superiority over the obviously stupid country boy. They made no effort to hide their irritation at being interviewed a second time within a week, and were impatient about the way they had to keep going over each bit of information so he could catch on.

I overheard one of the bank clerks tell another that "this fellow who couldn't catch a cold, much less the nigger who robbed them, was wasting *their* time." They had important entries to make in their books. "And at eighty-five cents an hour, too," the other teller added seriously.

This wasn't lost on the Cracker, but he didn't seem to

mind. On the way to the next interview he drawled out his impressions and advice. "Now, don't go trying the rural southern boy approach, it won't work for you. This is an individual thing and has got to be developed over a period of time. You should try out a bunch of different ways with these little stolen car cases they'll give you; don't let it bother you if nothing seems to work at first, you'll find something good in time. Then you can use it when you get a big jewel case, or security, or bank robbery. But don't just sit back and be afraid to try anything because you think people'll laugh at you. That don't make no difference. People are more likely to talk to someone while they're laughing than when they're scared."

He went on and on. I was amazed, because Spence never talked in the office, hardly said "hello" in the morning. His words were clumsy at times, they didn't reflect much formal education, they weren't in proper Bureau language, but to a new agent starved for some practical advice on investigations they were "apples of gold in pictures of silver."

He took me to another bank that had been burglarized the night before. The agents were still working the crime scene for latent fingerprints when we arrived.

"Boy, come over here." That was the only thing I didn't like about him—he always called me boy. I walked over to the remains of a safe.

"Ordinarily, the fellows would check the safe itself for tool marks. Some of the good safe men have custom made tools which leave marks of character, like put'n their name on the safe door.

"But, it won't do no good here, this is a 'blow job'."

I jerked around to see if he was kidding me. He was dead serious.

"Now, boy, the safe crackers use several methods to get inside. This fellow used nitro and blew the door open. Others do a 'peel job' by drilling into one corner of the door then peeling off all the layers, and that takes a lot of time. The best way is a 'punch job,' but that takes skill. They drill holes around the combination lock, punch it back inside the safe, then they just swing open the door. And naturally, the great ones can open the safe by feeling the tumblers fall with their fingers. I'm looking for one of those guys right now."

We watched the other agents work for awhile. They used black powder for light surfaces, and white and colored powders for the black surface of the safe. After dusting lightly, they'd lift any prints by use of a sticky paper—almost like fly paper. Then they packaged, initialed and prepared them for mailing back to the lab in Washington while still at the scene. This prevented them from mixing up the evidence.

Spence got a ladder from the custodian and climbed up to inspect the ceiling; without touching the surrounding walls, he gently lifted off a grill covering a vent in the ceiling. The burglar had crawled through this large six foot vent, and had stood up just before dropping twenty feet to the floor leaving a heel print in the dust. He'd climbed back up with a rope, but had left another heel print on his exit out the ceiling vent. They took plaster casts of those heel prints and sent them to the FBI lab where they had on file all the manufacturers' samples. It was really impressive, they didn't miss a thing.

Spence and I didn't stop for dinner, we just went from lead to lead, but I didn't mind, I could have lasted all night without it. Then a little after seven that evening, Spence drove back to the garage, checked out of the office, and went home without a word.

"Isn't he supposed to dictate all those interviews, Wally, so they can be transcribed and typed up in his files?" I asked, back in the office.

"He'll dictate the ones that mean anything."

"The file will only show half the work that we did on the case." I protested because I wanted credit for all those interviews, too. Wally caught this right away, and set me straight.

"And the rest of us just go along for the ride, or conduct interviews over the telephone, and make it appear that we do two times as much work."

"That's right," I sheepishly agreed. . . . "Doesn't anyone but Spence care whether they solve a case?"

"Sure, Norm. But we like our jobs, and want to continue to be agents, and to do that we must win the battle of paper, and survive the inspections. The Director cares more about the case load than the number of cases you've solved. We can always close out a tricky case, without solving it. He loves high case loads and lots of voluntary overtime—VOT. Our most impressive statistics are obtained from stolen auto cases, checks, ITSP's, army deserters, unemployment compensation frauds. That's where we get our bulk of new cases opened, high case loads, fines and recoveries—we get a lot of convictions from these too. What carries the office are the little cases that add up to large statistics. When I turn a Cuban agent it doesn't help our statistics much. Eaton Alderton can open, solve and convict in two hundred and fifty unemployment frauds in the same length of time. The boys on the auto squad can recover a half million dollars' worth of autos in the time it takes the top jewel thief program to get one conviction. So you see the most glamorous jobs in the Bureau aren't the most important."

"I guess if you honestly feel that the Director's statistics are more important than putting a stop to crime in the U. S. then you're right, but who really feels that way? I know I don't, Wally."

Post tried to explain it to me. "Everyone who is concerned about staying in the Bureau and collecting their retirement feels that way. And it's not as bad as you might think at first. Isn't it better that agents like Spence and some of the boys on security put up with the system and stay in the Bureau? What if they quit? Then no one would be working these important cases."

"The Director knows what works as far as Congress goes," Wally continued, "and we go along with it because we have no other choice. It's not the Director's fault; he has to give the Congress what they like, and they like statistics. We are a perfect example of a government executive Bureau directed by Congress who are in turn elected by the people. This Bureau is merely following the direction of the American people. Democracy in its purest form." Wally was just giving me a speech, so I didn't listen to what he was saying. But I did listen when he turned and looked at me and talked more slowly.

"Why can't we all be like Spence?" I countered. The Cracker didn't put up with any red tape. He did so much work he only reported half of it, but he was genuinely content.

"You've got to produce, you have to be exceptional. Spence has a facility for solving bank cases, he's built up some good informants over the years. But he's different—he has a special talent. Most of the rest of us have to win the battle of paper, of statistics, in order to survive as agents."

Post grabbed a pamphlet from the top drawer of his desk. "Here's what's important to this Bureau. The first thing the

Director talks about when he appears before Congress is the replacement of automobiles. 'The Bureau will have an estimated 1,445 vehicles which will have met the government's minimum replacement standards. Funds, however, are requested to purchase only 501, the same number as allowed under the Bureau's approved appropriation for the fiscal year 1964. We will continue to obtain further service from the other cars.'

"Second is, fines and recoveries. 'The total of fines, savings and recoveries recorded during the fiscal year represents a return of $1.37 for each $1.00 of direct funds appropriated to the Bureau during the fiscal year!' This is why the auto theft squad is more important around here than the intelligence squad: they get the much needed statistics in fines and recoveries by jacking up the values of the cars we recover."

"Sounds like the auto squad does all the work. But do they really lie about the values?" I asked him.

"It takes sophistication and experience, Norm. Of course they don't lie themselves. Here's how the squad works, and they'll be the first to tell you. An entire case can be worked over the phone if necessary. First you receive a call from the Miami Beach police department. They have located an abandoned auto with out-of-state license plates on it. They'll even crawl underneath the car and get the secret motor number for you. With that information you call the National Auto Theft Bureau, a private corporation, and they'll tell you where the auto was stolen and notify the owner. You then get the police officer to tow the car to a garage, give you an estimate of the recovery value. If you have maintained the right kind of liaison with him he'll be more than generous about the value of the auto. You don't estimate yourself, you merely quote the officer's appraisal. The rest can be taken care of by dictating a few leads and airtels to interview the owner of the car for possible suspects, and you haven't even gotten your hands dirty."

Wally looked back at the pamphlet he held. " 'Identification of fingerprints.' We don't have to worry about that, that's Washington's problem."

" 'Field justification. There has been no letup in the volume of the field work which we must handle. New peaks have been reached in several classifications of criminal work.' " Wally looked up from the report. "This means we have to open new cases at an increasing rate every year. But don't start opening a lot of cases until you check with your supervisor, because if we increase too *much,* then it makes it impossible to show an increase the next year. As I said, this takes a little sophistication."

" 'Overtime services. Over the years our investigative personnel have been performing very substantial overtime services. During the fiscal year this overtime amounted to an aggregate of 3,175,081 hours, an average of 1 hour and 14 minutes a day on the part of each member of our investigative staff every workday of the year, in excess of the 1 hour and 12 minutes per day for which fringe benefits are paid. Had it been necessary to employ the additional 1,526 agents represented by this overtime, the cost would have been an estimated $17,293,429.' That, my friend, is the cause of all our time card difficulties." Wally turned the page.

" 'The average caseload per agent is presently 22, a year ago it was 20.' We have to make sure our caseload per agent increases every year. To do this, refrain from closing a case that you could close by a letter until you get some new ones; this will help keep your case load up.

"It's really not complicated, Norm. We have a responsibility to supply the Director with the statistics that he needs to get what we all want from Congress. If it interferes with what we personally think is best for the Bureau, that is too bad, we are just workers, not the leaders. Chain of command, you know."

I had become at ease with Wally. I knew I could be entirely candid when I asked him questions about the F.B.I. But in a fit of temper I overstepped the bounds of our friendship. "How do you and Spence and the other working agents in this office put up with this farce? Aren't you disgusted? Doesn't your conscience bother you? How do you look each other square in the eye?"

Wally smiled, "Ollestad, you're young, inexperienced and cocky. But remember one thing, you're not the Director of the F.B.I. You're just a young fellow who has signed a contract of employment and taken the oath that you will perform your duties as the Director tells you."

He was right and I was wrong and I knew it. I changed the subject.

"Wally, do you think you can fix it up so that I can go out with Spence again tomorrow?"

"Sure thing," he said, smiling.

The following day I was back with Spence. A former Georgia state trooper before joining the Bureau, he readily admitted his deep racial prejudices.

How can a guy so hampered with ignorance have such great success in solving his cases, I wondered, watching him shuffling through the office, mumbling "hello" to most of the secretaries, some of the agents, completely ignoring the SAC and ASAC and the supervisors.

But when Spence was working a case he lost himself, he died, he forgot his "bringing up." People became important to him; he shared their thoughts because they had secrets, information he needed.

He shouldered their problems a little; didn't judge their mean petty aspirations, but offered subtle, indirect encouragement.

The "stool pigeons" he interviewed, for the most part criminals and bums, changed when he was around. Not one informant asked for money in exchange for the information. It didn't occur to Spence to give it, they didn't expect it. The job, the problem was the thing that they both had a duty to solve, they had no choice but to find a solution. The most astounding change was in Spence himself. He lost all prejudices, allowed no preconceived ideas about people or their behavior to temper each individual appraisal. He would point out the failings of a bank official who was fraternizing with one of the female tellers as quickly as he would those strong feelings of Americanism on the part of some of the "blacks" he interviewed. He was a completely different man. Tolerant, talkative, sympathetic. He and I drank beer (against Bureau rules) with the greasiest of Negroes, ate with the dressed-up ones—educated folk who were very careful about their English and very careful not to call him sir, and who, with effort, managed always to call both of us by our first names. The Cracker let Negro children ride in the Bureau car with the siren going full blast. He enjoyed it so much that I didn't learn until later that he was working on a case at the time. His eyes would change too, they became much lighter, not so cloudy. He really needed the Bureau. In any other job he'd be just another red-necked southerner *all* the time.

We visited some of his informants, the prostitutes on Miami Beach, not quite the classic Southern women, but

Spence treated them with kindness. "Treat all women like queens, boy, and to their lik'en you'll be a king."

But the Georgia Cracker didn't always work by informants. One day we received a radio call that the Central Bank and Trust Company had just been robbed. This call had emanated from the Miami field office, and had gone out to all the F.B.I. cars in the area. As Spence sped our car toward the victimized bank, I noticed several F.B.I. radio cars driven by the "drones" of the Miami field office—Eaton T. Alderton, Wilson S. Murray and John D. Illinger. The Cracker saw them too. They were driving *away* from the Central Bank and Trust Company—away from the scene of the robbery. I later learned it was because they feared if they went immediately to the scene of the bank robbery, they would be the "No. 1 man" and would have to take charge of the bank robbery investigation. The "No. 1 man" had the responsibility of solving the initial stages of the bank robbery. It bothered me, but I didn't say anything, and if it bothered Spence I couldn't tell by the preoccupation written on his face. We were the first representatives of the F.B.I. to arrive at the Central Bank and Trust Company and the Georgia Cracker was the "No. 1 man." Spence methodically obtained descriptions of the two men who had robbed the bank. By combining different versions of the six bank tellers who had seen the robbery, Spence was able to give a general description to the agents who, after enough pause to insure that they wouldn't be the "No. 1 man," arrived at the scene. The older of the two robbers—the leader—was missing two fingers on his left hand; was a tall Caucasian—had brown straight hair, brown eyes, and wore a business suit. The older criminal had been calmly efficient and had presented the teller at window No. 3 with a bank money bag and a note made out of clipped newspaper print demanding all the money in bills of denominations of $100.00 or under. The teller had thoughtfully included in the currency that he surrendered to the criminal an "FBI bank robbery package"—a bundle of currency, the serial numbers of each bill having been pre-recorded and kept in a separate drawer by the clerk. The "package" also contained several $2.00 bills. The consensus of opinion of the witnesses was that the smaller, younger member of the robbery team bore a striking resemblance in facial appearance to the older member.

After Spence had dispersed several F.B.I. agents as they arrived at the bank to search the neighborhood for a description of the bank robber's automobile, Spence took me over to the corner of the bank.

"Now listen, boy, I don't want you to operate like this the first time you get a bank robbery case, but I'm going to do a little speculatin'. Now then, if I was old Three Finger—the man that robbed the bank—he's only got three fingers on his left hand—if I was him—and I've heard of him before; he robs his banks in Chicago, Illinois—but anyway, boy, if I was him and I was robbing a bank at 11:00 A.M. and I had either my son or one of my kin folks with me, well to show the boy what a big man I was, I would go all the way. Now just speculatin', if I was from out of town and I had this boy with me and I was the man that robbed the Central Bank, I'd case the bank in the morning at 10:00, then to show the youngster that was with me that I wasn't scared, I'd go right around the corner, order myself a cup of coffee and come right back and rob that bank."

Spence was smiling, his happiness spread through his entire face. Then he backed up a little.

"Now don't you go telling any of the other agents about this in case it don't work out, boy. As I said, it's just speculatin', that's all I'm doing."

We used the "grid method search" to comb the neighborhood near the Central Bank. We started out having coffee at the nearest shop to the bank and then spread out, covering each city block or "grid" as we emanated away from the bank. We even had a late lunch that day in a coffee shop.

After about two coffees, three tomato juices (I'm not a coffee drinker), two ice cream cones, and lunch, we hit. It was exciting. I felt as if I had helped crack the case myself, although all I did was tag along with the Cracker. We got our lead on the bank robbers in a building which was half a coffee shop and half a Chinese laundry. The oriental waitress who served Spence his twelfth cup of coffee knew who we were talking about immediately. "Of course, a man with two fingers missing on one of his hands and his son were in here this morning for coffee."

"How do you remember so quickly?" I asked suspiciously. "The man said he was interested in Chinese art," the girl answered, "and that he was in the business. He gave me his home address. He's here in Miami on business but he lives in Chicago, Illinois."

I couldn't believe it. It was a stroke of pure luck, but of course the pure luck was made possible by the speculation of a canny old hunter, Special Agent I. A. Spence. It was folly for the bank robber to have given his brother's address in Chicago, Illinois, to a waitress not ten blocks from the bank he had robbed, but it was folly brought on by pride and by egotism, the same reckless abandon that made him insane enough to pull an armed robbery in the first place. Apparently Spence had picked up a little of that scent and that's what led us to the criminal's mistake.

"We've got 'em now, boy," Spence told me, "it's only a matter of time. I'll send out leads to the Chicago office and if Three Fingers returns in a couple of days, we'll be waiting for him. I have an idea that one of those two dollar bills will nail him."

I respectfully disagreed. "Are you kidding? He'll avoid those bills like poison, they're a dead giveaway."

"That's true, son," Spence agreed, "but he'll tip bartenders with 'em, pay off loans with those two dollar bills—he won't be able to burn 'em or throw 'em away. And most of the people he gives 'em to won't know they're stolen, and they'll keep those bills, and when the case breaks and he's caught, we'll line these people up. It'll make a good case in court; I'll bet we can trace him right back here to Miami with those lucky two dollar bills."

Of course the Cracker's prediction came true. Within two months Three Fingers had been arrested and convicted of the robbery.

The Cracker was definitely not what you'd call a "swinger," but he sure did fool me several times. Once we picked up the trail of a relatively new but talented bank burglar. We found out from one of Spence's informants that the young man, who had successfully pulled three bank jobs in the Miami area alone, shacked up occasionally with a waitress who worked at "Jeff's Place" on Flagler Street over on the Miami side. We drove over to the bar early one evening only to find it was the waitress's night off. We checked the apartment where the criminal and the waitress had their parties, but it was vacant. The manager told us that the waitress also had a key to the room, and we figured she must know our fugitive pretty well, so we drove over to her residence a few miles away.

I knocked on the door, and a man answered.

"Does a Mildred Sloan live here?" I asked.

"Yes," the man answered, "I'm her husband. Well . . . uh . . . yes, she does, won't you come in?"

As Mildred came into the living room, her husband asked warily, "What's this all about, Millie?"

She didn't answer, so I began to question her. "Here is a photograph of the man we are looking for. We are special agents of the F.B.I. That's Mr. Spence, and I'm Mr. Ollestad."

Spence shot a look at me as if to say, "It's about time you introduced us." Spence was letting me handle this part of the investigation.

"Have you ever seen this man?" I continued.

From her expression I knew she recognized him. She almost dropped the photo, but whined, "No, I'm sorry, I haven't ever seen this man before."

I was hopping mad. "Hadn't seen him!" I thought. She'd been spending every other night in the guy's apartment until three and four in the morning. The woman was *deliberately* lying, trying to cover up.

"What's this all about?" the husband shouted at her angrily. I was about to tell him what it was all about when Spence took over. "Now, sir," he told the husband, "I'm awfully sorry to have bothered you and your wife at this evening hour. It's merely that your wife works at 'Jeff's Place' and this man comes in there occasionally. We thought that maybe your wife could recognize him, but I see that's not the case. Thanks to both of you for being so patient with us. I hope we haven't disturbed your evening."

Millie looked at Spence as if he had just given her a million dollars, maybe more than a million dollars.

Spence and I left the house without another word. When we reached the car, I tried to find out what he was doing.

"Can I ask what you did that for?" I queried.

"Nope," he answered. "Boy, you're just going to have to learn to keep your eyes and ears open and your mouth shut for awhile until you learn."

The next day we both returned to 'Jeff's' and found a staunch ally, a new informant for the F.B.I. Millie was willing to do anything for us. There was even a slight chance, I felt, that she'd change her ways and stop cheating on her husband. She made a positive ident of our fugitive, and vowed she'd tip us off the next time he came around.

Then Spence explained it to me. "No amount of money would do it, boy. She thought she was in love with him, and women have a greater allegiance to love than to money. But maybe she realizes what she had been doing. She's not going to escape the dull dreary life she leads working at 'Jeff's,' then going home to be beaten by her husband, she's not going to escape all that by carrying on with that flash-in-the-pan criminal. May be exciting to her at first, but she knows there's a better way to get out of a rut, and it ain't the way she tried to do it."

On schedule, Millie called us two nights later. Our criminal was holed up over on the beach side, in a motel.

Sometimes Special Agent Spence was so cautious that it bordered on cowardice. I expected us to rush to the motel in Miami Beach and arrest the fugitive, but instead, Spence, without a word of explanation to me, drove us both back to the Bureau garage.

I followed him as he left the car, and went back into the office and checked out a pair of handcuffs, which he placed in his coat, right under his arm pit, one shackle running down his coat sleeve, the other next to his body. I thought for sure that we would leave the office then, but instead he went into the file room, pulled the case file on the criminal that we were setting out to apprehend and thumbed through it for about twenty minutes. As I paced nervously back and forth in the room, I glanced impatiently over his shoulder and noticed the caption, "Armed and dangerous."

The fugitive was also wanted for several bank jobs in Atlanta, Georgia. He was only twenty-three.

When we finally did leave the office and headed for the fugitive's hideout, Spence insisted on driving slowly and without talking to me. He seemed to be mulling over the information he had just read. As we reached the motel and made an identification on the fugitive's automobile parked in front of one of the rooms, Spence took me into the manager's office at the motel's entrance instead of going in and arresting the criminal as I thought he would. The manager told us as far as he knew, the fugitive was alone in the room, and identified him from a photograph Spence had picked up at the office.

I got the uneasy feeling that Special Agent I. A. Spence was afraid to go in and arrest the guy, the way he was stalling around. Finally we took our positions near the door of the fugitive's room and I thought we were going in, but we only circled around to the back of the room and discovered there was no rear entrance, just a louvered bathroom window. When Spence took me back to the Bureau car and radioed the Dade County sheriff's office, I was convinced that the Cracker was a coward. While we had been fooling around, getting background at the field office and showing photographs to the manager, the criminal could have escaped.

Spence spoke to me in a whisper, "I'm doing two things here, boy," he drawled. I wondered how he could stop and give me advice in such a tense situation. Why is he stalling, I asked myself again. . . .

". . . doing two things. Number one, I have a running deal with a sergeant over at Dade County. I let him in on anything I come up with that involves a bank job in his territory, and he lets me know when he discovers one of my men. You see, the burglary of a national bank is also a crime in the state of Florida, so he gets credit too if he helps capture the fugitive."

Spence paused a moment, listening. He went over and checked the back window, crept up to the front door for a moment, then came back.

"Second thing. I know that fellow inside that room. Unless he's with someone else I can take him without any shooting, so I don't want you drawing your revolver."

Then at that point I realized that the Cracker wasn't a coward after all. I just hadn't had enough experience in law enforcement to appreciate how good he really was.

The sheriff from Dade County arrived and burned the difference between the F.B.I. and the local police forever in my mind. The sergeant was fat, had the proverbial large abdomen held up by a large brown wide belt which was hitched underneath, and the first thing he wanted to do was blow the front door down, fire a tear gas bomb into the room and shoot the kid when he came out.

Spence cut him off. "Charles"—Charles Downes was the fat cop's name—"Charles, I've already got it. You go cover the back window and get him if he comes out." Spence knew the fugitive could never open that louvered window in time to try to escape out of it. "Now you stay there, Charles, until we get him, because if you move, he'll get out the back window."

Charles Downes drew his weapon and crept around to the back window of the motel. I prepared to go into the room, but Spence still wasn't ready. He went back a second time to the hotel manager's office and told me to watch the front door while he was gone. He came back with a large pail of water.

I started to ask him what he was doing.

"Mr. Spence, what the hell. . . ."

The Cracker didn't have time to be diplomatic with me.

"Now, listen, boy, you be still and just watch and do what I tell you."

That shut me up quickly and I watched Spence. He crept up to the door of the motel and began slowly pouring the bucket of water underneath the door in such a way it flowed into the motel room where the fugitive had locked himself. When about half the bucket had been emptied underneath the door and into the room, the criminal's curiosity got the better of him. We heard the double lock slowly turn and at that moment I wished I could have had my .38 revolver in my hand instead of in my holster. But I changed my mind when the criminal opened the door; he was alone and as small as I was. The Cracker whipped the cuffs out of his coat and had them slapped on the young man before he'd finished saying, "The F.B.I.—you're under arrest."

We searched the room. It was empty. He had spent all his money on prostitutes and a new Corvette, and had no weapons or burglar's tools.

"You're going to handcuff him to the car, aren't you, Spence?" Charles Downes yelled as he came puffing around from the back of the motel. "He's a bad one."

Apparently old Charles Downes felt that criminals didn't get punished enough in prison, so he wanted to do a little on the way to jail.

"We'll take care of him, Charles," Spence said, as he searched the fugitive, then cuffed his hands behind him. Spence put me in the back seat with him, and we transported the criminal to the Dade County jail, with Charles Downes following close behind us in his sheriff's squad car.

"Don't take Charles too hard boy, he gets overly enthused at times. And remember, don't never handcuff a man to the inside of a moving automobile, for if you have an accident he won't be able to free himself."

The criminal was a bitter, young wise guy. He was in many ways just like a young man I was to get involved with later, because of my yen for surfing. He spoke with bravado—something he had lacked when Spence had arrested him.

"You guys got by with it this time, but next time I'm going to hold my court right out in the street."

"Naw, you don't mean that son, you don't mean that," Spence said.

"Do you know Walker at the Ojus Electric Plant?" the Cracker continued. "Well, I went out there lookin' for you the other day and he said you're the best machinist he ever had, and that if you do go to jail you can have your old job back when you get out. That's what the man said, if you want to know the truth."

"Walker is a stupid ass," the young man shot back.

"That's what the man said, you can have it back," Spence repeated.

In the short time that I followed Spence, I was unable to understand the feeling he had for the criminals he hunted.

He respected their intelligence, and in its absence, their cunning, their knowledge of human nature that allowed them to escape capture momentarily. The Cracker would be the last to say that these criminals were prisoners of their own mind, mentally ill. He scoffed at psychiatrists, reformers and liberals. Yet he seemed to know instinctively that the fugitives were captives of some sort, because when he busted them and turned them in, there was no acrimony—no personal hatred. He put them in jail—nothing could stop him from doing that, not even a paper pushing bureaucracy, but he didn't hate them. Even when he had to kill a man one day.

# 19

There were things I would like to forget ever happened in the Bureau. I would like to forget how we all treated the two Negroes in the office, Leo, the Negro F.B.I. agent, and Jim, the Negro clerk.

Leo was what everyone called "a good nigger."

"What squad is Leo on, Wally?" I asked Wally Post one day.

"Not exactly on any squad. He'll clean and blue up all the agents' pistols for them, arrest a few fugitives in nigger town, and is available twenty-four hours a day to chauffeur the Director around when he comes to Miami for the races."

"How does he stand it?"

"He wouldn't trade places with you or me."

I found out Wally was right, Leo had no reason to be unhappy. He had only a high school education, had served as a Bureau clerk, and after 10 years of faithful service had been blessed by the Director with a special agent's job—he didn't even have to go through the training for new agents at the Academy.* He earned a higher salary than any other Negro in the south. The white agents envied his role as court jester, keeping the office happy with jokes, and his easy

_____

*Leo wasn't allowed to attend. The first two Negro agents to be allowed to go through the New Agents' Training at the F.B.I. Academy in Quantico, Virginia, attended the Academy in 1964, 29 years after the Academy's inception.

manner. The only time he experienced the day to day pressure and harassment of his fellow Special Agents was when the Director came to town. He then became a true agent of the Bureau, a legitimate buddy, a comrade under fire, one of the boys, an equal—and he hated every minute of it.

The Director's Cadillac was kept in the field office garage. Since it was used only to drive the Director, once or twice a year, it was hell to keep it polished and in good running condition. Leo spent hours running the engine in the garage, and constantly badgered the mechanics to keep it tuned.

As soon as the racing season began at Tropical Park, Leo would start to tighten up in anticipation, and would suffer until the last race at Gulf Stream Park, which meant that the season was over. But his misery became acute when the Director landed. As we agents had trouble sleeping during a field office inspection, old Leo would show up in the office morning after morning during his driving tour, his face a study in worried, wrinkled black.

The Director always stayed at the Gulf Stream Hotel on Miami Beach, where they always picked up his tab. Leo would drive over to the Gulf Stream every morning, then drive the Director to the race track. Ordinarily, Leo would have enjoyed the detail, because he loved to play the horses and there was nothing else to do for the five or six hours that he waited for the Director, but he never played.

He would sit and run the Cadillac in the parking lot, hoping to keep it running and in tune, and invariably something would go wrong. As soon as the feature race was over he would fire up the Cadillac and wait for the running of the last race with the engine going, but even this procedure was not enough to forestall the inevitable. Several times during each visit, the Director would tell Leo that if the sputtering car did not start up immediately that he, Leo, would be fired and would no longer be with "all those gallant agents who daily face death to carry out the duties thrust upon the F.B.I."

During these crises, Leo would have gladly become a Bureau clerk once more—would have willingly surrendered any amount of dignity he had left after cleaning all our guns for a little assurance that he would not be fired.

But when the Director went back to the Seat of Government, as everyone put it, "the 'shine' would shine again." Once more Leo would delight us agents with war stories and colorful anecdotes of the Director—once more become an envied man, a happy, popular man.

That was not exactly the case with Jim, the Negro clerk. He was very good-looking, a fact very disconcerting to the young southern flowers composing the secretarial force in the office. A few harbored a secret, fleeting thought about him occasionally, and hated him for it.

Everyone discovered six months after he was hired that "he didn't know his place like Leo." But nothing could be done about it. It was true, everyone agreed, that ordinarily something could have been cooked up "Bureau style," with the appropriate documentation to prove that he was morally undesirable, but for Jim this was impossible because Fife, who was of course supervisor, had interviewed and OK'd him for Bureau service. If Jim were found to be wanting at this late date, after his probation had expired, it would be a reflection on Fife's perceptive abilities when interviewing new applicants, and disciplinary action would have to be taken against both, if any at all. What made the situation even worse was that Jim was to be made the second Negro special agent in the office "if the civil rights thing got too hot."

"You're just ruining your chances, boy," Leo told him constantly.

"You're too old, Leo, you believe all the stuff they've been telling you all these years—no use talking about it," Jim would counter.

As Fife said repeatedly, "There are twenty-seven Negro agents out of 6,200. We didn't use to have any out in the field. It may get worse because the civil rights groups are pushing hard. We've got to expose the movement for what it is if we are to continue the Bureau on its present high plane. The way to do this is to discredit their organizations by pointing out the large number of commies that are in the leadership. One of their leaders, Martin Luther King, even attended a conference of Communists and the Alabama authorities caught him red handed. They've got more than a representative percentage of their race in the Bureau as it is. There aren't that many educated qualified Negroes in their percentage of the American population, 27 is too many already."

Fife's favorite joke was always given at the top of his voice so Leo and Jim could eat a little of that Jim Crow stuff once in awhile. "You know what President Kennedy says, boys, if you don't work with vigah, you'll be replaced by a niggah."

Jim never did anything that showed it bothered him, but he still made everybody mad. He was a college graduate. One of those "nigger colleges." Gave the impression, without saying it, that he thought his Bachelor of Arts was equivalent to a degree from the University of Miami, "intellectually, that is," and everyone in the office knew that was impossible. The only stenographer with college experience—flunked out of Miami—constantly illustrated the rigid standards at the University of Miami. "It was possible to be given a 'D' in a subject, even though you did all the homework assignments and all the outside reading." This precious bit of information was always given loudly and within Jim's hearing, but the only reaction she ever received from him was one of almost delirious mirth. Most of the time he didn't notice. He was just too independent, the girls could never catch him wistfully looking in their direction. He did what he was told, left the office promptly at five P.M., didn't attempt to hang around with anyone, never tried to cover up his "inherent laziness" by working at top speed all day. He took all the coffee breaks that the clerks were allowed, and was never unaccountably absent.

It was especially galling that he had no trouble mixing with the special agents with the ease of an equal. Most of the SA's were too worried, too busy building a paper fortress of protection to bother too much about Jim's color. They enjoyed the way he told jokes, and he would laugh at theirs, but not like Leo—only if they were good. Jim's stock room was a good place to try out a new joke, unless they had a sure thing. Jim called the older agents "mister" and us younger ones by our first names. I felt much more at ease with him than with Leo.

Although the agents could tolerate Jim, the clerical staff definitely could not. "After all," as Miss Long, the chief clerk put it, "we're the ones who really have to work with him day after day. Even on hot days, when the smell of his sweat stinks up the whole stock room. I wouldn't think of asking one of our young girls to go into such a room. You know how a nigger stinks when he sweats."

Miss Opal Long, the chief clerk, literally ran the office— that is, when she wasn't worrying about the fact that it "wasn't safe for a woman to walk the streets of Miami these days, with all the Cubans and smart-aleck niggers about."

Gaunt and ugly, she was undoubtedly the only female in the city that didn't have to worry about being accosted, but she constantly entertained the possibility.

In the battle of F.B.I. statistics, the SAC knew that he was most vulnerable personally in the paper and correspondence area, and the chief clerk took care of all of that, leaving him free to concentrate on personnel problems, real and fabricated. Opal Long doctored up some of the records with his tacit consent and the office was thus able to present a facade to the Seat of Government, to enable them in return to prepare their own for presentation to the Director. Mr. Hoover made good use of the material. He could "make figures come alive, breathe life into cold statistics."

Opal liked me. I think she had an idea that I knew someone in Hollywood and that if she played her cards right she'd be a movie star.

"Did you want to talk to me, Miss Long?"

"Yes, Mr. Ollestad, it's about that applicant that you wrote a recommendation for, George Albin. Some more information came in on him and I thought you'd be interested." She handed me a file, then left the room.

I looked through the reports. My recommendation was on the second page. "George is a new acquaintance. A graduate student at the University of Miami. He majors in foreign language—Chinese. In the short time I have known him, I have found him to be a loyal American of good moral character." Although Albin had only a Master's degree at the time he applied for the Bureau, I knew that his knowledge of foreign languages would qualify him much more than the clerks that had composed part of my New Agents' Class.

As I leafed through the subsequent inserts in the official

Bureau files, I saw Supervisor Fife's report. As I read it a fat stomach came into my periphery. It belonged to Fife. I felt guilty since I'd already made a recommendation in the case, and it wasn't too good of an idea to be looking at what the subsequent investigation had turned up. I tried to casually unload the file on the nearest desk and leave the room. Fife stopped me. "Mr. Ollestad, looks like you've misjudged the situation."

I knew enough at this stage of my Bureau career to remain silent. I stood still and smiled into Fife's fat face, fixed my stare on his blue-tinged jowls hanging over the stiff collar of his starched white shirt.

"This fellow you wrote the report on, he's not agent material. Look at this." He took the reports out of my hand, read from them. "One of his former employers in New York just last week says, 'He was a poor worker, wouldn't make deliveries on time, was always reading books during the breaks and lunch hour, was very aloof to customers coming into the store. Period of employment, June 7th to August 31st, 1958. We can't approve his application with all this derogatory information in his personnel file."

Stupid, this was just a summer job, you shouldn't give it that much weight, I thought. I didn't say anything though.

"Now, look," Fife continued, "what if something were to happen, what if he did something wrong when he became an agent, shot somebody, or quit right away. If I approved him I'd get a kick back because of this in his file. He's not punctual; you know what the Director says about punctuality. 'Punctuality is the best policy!' "

I thought to myself that the supervisor was so used to quoting the Director that he substituted his thoughts for

Hoover's. J. Edgar would never say anything as stupid as that, punctuality is the best policy! Jesus!

Fife went on, "Reading books all the time, that's the kind of individual that means trouble. History shows they are anarchists and such. One of those fellows that read all the time in coffee houses started World War One. We can only approve those applicants who have no derogatory reports in their files that can hang me . . . uh, us . . . if anything goes wrong with his Bureau career. So I'm certainly not going to approve this guy's application, and I will not recommend him to the Bureau. Even though they have to review his application, no one at the Seat of Government would dare present this applicant to the Director if I recommend against it. I have nothing against this kid personally even though he is part Jewish, but it's just a matter of protecting ourselves."

I had just seen Fife's report of his interview with Albin dated a month before, and his conclusion that "Albin would make excellent agent material." But I was careful not to let the smile slip from my face and I kept silent about my discovery.

"As a matter of fact," Fife stated, "I'm going to correct a few typographical errors which appear in my report, and I suggest that you re-write yours and reflect that he is not qualified."

The petty, unjust request hit me hard, and I was mad that Albin was going to be rejected. I felt myself get hot all over. My lower lip became unstable. I knew I had just lost control, but I didn't care. I croaked through a suddenly parched throat. "I think I'll leave mine as it is." A picture of my fist rammed into the supervisor's flabby cheek flashed into my mind as I stepped forward with head lowered, my eyes fixed on Fife's belt buckle which was almost buried in the shirt-covered fat of his midsection. I was going to hit him and leave the Bureau in a blaze of self-satisfaction.

But I walked right into Miss Long as she burst into the room. "Mr. Ollestad . . . Mr. Fife, I've got a very important matter to talk to you about. . . . Did I interrupt something?"

"No, it's taken care of. What is it?" Fife said.

"It's about Jim and I don't want to discuss it in front of the girls on the staff because you know how they all love him so, and treat him like one of us, but I feel I must speak out."

The supervisor nodded toward me hoping to defer the discussion until I had left, but Opal didn't understand.

"Oh, it's all right to talk about it with an agent. It's about Jim and the office party. It's scheduled for the end of summer down at the Biscayne Beach park. You know how we all look forward to it every year, even the agents, but especially the girls and boys under me. They work so hard all year so they can go to this party. And of course Leo never comes, and we got that beach on the assumption that neither Leo or Jim would come over because they're very strict about niggers. It's a brand new beach, everything's clean. When I was over making the arrangements, the park official happened to tell me about the good old days when no niggers were allowed over on the beach after sundown unless they were working over there, and I knew he was hinting, so I told him not to worry about niggers at our party.

"I hate to think of what could happen if Jim tries to swim over there. I'm against violence and the flaunting of the law."

With that plea, she hesitated a moment. But with me present, Fife was silent. The chief clerk misunderstood. She then felt she had to go on to drive home her point. "Something has to be done. Not for my sake, or not because any-one in the office doesn't want him to come—we all love him dearly . . . think of the embarrassment to us and most espe-cially to him when he is kicked out. I was afraid of him, so I passed around the memo for the two dollar deposit early this year, to put my mind at rest, and Jim paid the money. I don't see how he can expect to go to the beach park when he has lived in this neighborhood all his life."

Opal Long was still whimpering about Jim when I slipped out of the room. I was very thankful to her. She had given me a reprieve, and had saved me from being fired from the F.B.I. because of my childish fit of temper. Of course Fife hadn't noticed what I had on my mind, so I was perfectly in the clear as long as I didn't stick my nose into the office party crisis. I'd lost any sense of righteous indignation that I had carried into the F.B.I. long before this incident occurred; I knew that kind of an attitude just caused trouble. I was more experienced, less naively idealistic now. I let Jim fend for himself. There wasn't anything that I could have done, anyway. At least I don't think there was anything I could have done. I put the whole affair out of my mind and tried to learn to become a better agent.

Part of keeping sharp as an agent involved marksmanship practice. Every month we field agents had to qualify on the practice pistol course. We had to fire .38 revolvers from various positions—from the hip, lying on the ground, from behind barricades. We also had to load three times within a limited period of time, in order to get twenty rounds off over the course. Tuesday was my day for firing on the range and I got stuck with Special Agent Eaton Alderton. He had really gotten to be a bird dog—seemed to be with me every-where I went. But I enjoyed the pistol range, even with him.

It was a release for me to get out and talk with all the agents in a relaxed atmosphere. During the lunch hour one of the fellows took out some clubs and we all pitched golf balls back and forth across the range. For the first time since arriving in Miami, I was right in with the rest of my fellow agents as an equal, hitting iron shots over the targets. It was wonderful, the buzz and click of each shot, taking a firm deep divot of green healthy grass just after popping the ball.

Alderton didn't join us. "Why didn't you hit a few, Eaton?" I asked when the lunch period was over.

"I was studying the manual on the use of the sub machine gun," he answered.

I looked right into his face in disgust. Alderton had spent the whole lunch hour sunning himself on one of the benches, with no agent's handbook in sight. "You're so used to fibbing you don't know when to tell the truth," I mumbled to myself.

"What?" he asked.

"Nothing."

In the afternoon, I started having trouble scoring on the pistol course. As I approached a failing score, I tensed up and started bucking shots all over the range. I just made it by five points, to the obvious pleasure of the rest of the agents. They played it for laughs, but I was furious, mostly at myself.

Alderton was needling me as we drove back to the office to check out for the day. "Well, this pistol range isn't as easy as you thought it would be, huh, Ollestad?"

"Cut it out, Eaton. I saw you cheating on the course, taking more time than was allowed. If you'd gone through in regulation time you'd score a lot lower yourself."

"Are you insinuating that Kellan didn't run the firearms instruction properly?" he asked me.

"I'm saying that he didn't see you fudging on the time when you went through the course."

"Oh, you're saying that Kellan wasn't attentive and alert when administering the test."

"I mean *you*, not Joe Kellan," I said.

"Well, I fire until he says 'time'," he explained.

"And then you continue to fire until you've finished all your round," I shot back.

"If that were true, then both Joe and I would be busted, not just me," Eaton retorted.

"Forget it." That was my classic response to Eaton Alderton—it didn't do any good to argue with him.

Two days later I was called into the Supervisor's office. Fife didn't waste any time. "Mr. Ollestad, I'm very disappointed in you. You've got a good background, come from a good class of people, good education, but you're throwing it all away because of a bad attitude. Don't try to emulate some of those old timers on your squad. They aren't going anywhere in this Bureau—they take their orders from *me*."

Until a big case hits the office, I thought to myself, one that Washington takes "a personal interest" in, one that has to be solved right away. Then things change.

To look away from Fife now invited trouble, to talk might open something up, so I smiled and stared. I had learned all I needed to make my twenty years and retire.

"You've done several foolish things in the past few days. The major thing is accusing Joe Kellan the firearms instructor of cheating on the tests. That could get you fired very easily."

I avoided the trap set by Fife by keeping my silence. Anything I said in self-justification would only verify Alderton's story. At this point all the supervisor had was his informer's version, and that was by its very nature suspect. Fife had to protect himself, too, in case Eaton was stretching, or even deliberately misleading him. At least now I was certain that Eaton Alderton was a spy, or in F.B.I. terms, a "torpedo."

My silence caused Fife to do a little back peddling. "None of this is really important, Norm, and I'll personally stop any talk about your being fired. Now we know that the Director says 'We can only grow through constructive criticism,' but the kind of back biting you've been accused of was obviously not meant to help. Just for the future, Norm, okay?" He smiled the friendliest, most fatherly smile he could muster. "I'm trying to help you. You've had all the advantages in life and are throwing them away. I've had to work my way up—couldn't go to law school—barely got through college. You know what I did before I came into this Bureau? Sold vacuum cleaners. I'm damn glad to be where I am. Now, the only real reason I called you in here was to let you know that the Albin report is going into the Bureau tomorrow, and you're the only agent that wrote a favorable rec. I'm going to give you one more chance to change it."

I tried to be nonchalant, but I must have had a strange look on my face, because Fife kept explaining.

"See, Norm, it's the system, you've got to be able to adjust. Now, go back into the steno room and dictate another 302 on that Albin. I'm just trying to get you ready for the annual inspection, that's all."

Fife was kind of a funny guy. He impressed me as the type who demands strict discipline for his children, his cat and dog. He probably controlled their diet and exercise precisely; and yet all the while he was fat and self-indulgent. He continued on with his lecture.

"The Director every year sends 25 or more agent inspectors out from the Seat of Government to all the 57 field offices. We know in advance when the regular inspections are coming so we have a chance to get everything in order. But there are also surprise inspections that could come anytime, and then it's every man for himself. If they were to discover your interview, you'd have to justify it to the Director in a personal letter of explanation—why you didn't agree with twelve experienced agents in their appraisal of Albin. He likes unanimity in the Bureau, solidarity. And if you keep your nose clean and do everything you're told, sooner or later you'll get a personal letter of commendation from the Director."

I saw a chance to get out of Fife's office. "I never looked at it that way, thanks." As I walked through the door I fully intended to go directly down to the steno room and change my 302 report on Albin. But I hadn't signed up for a Steno so I had no one to type out a new 302. One thing after another came up and I never did get around to doctoring up Albin's report.

# 20

I worried and fretted for about a week over that 302 report. Finally, I couldn't stand the pressure, the self-inflicted pressure and Fife's harassment, so I tapped out. I became a surfer once more; only this time I was an F.B.I. agent surfer. And I took the time to look at what was happening around me.

Tropic spring dawned tepid and steaming into mid-April. I had been in Miami a little less than two months and it suddenly dawned on me that aside from a few weekend sorties over to Miami Beach I really hadn't been anywhere. I hadn't seen anything. There was a whole coastline to explore, an entire ocean out there with storms and winds . . . and that meant there had to be waves, too. Somewhere. And even in the face of the silent sea off Miami Beach I took the gamble and sent home for my surfboard. A week later it arrived.

With my surfboard strapped to the roof of my Volkswagen I once more prowled the coastline in search of surf . . . on weekends. The land was lush and green and much more deserted than any I had ever known. I stopped in the tiny shanty towns that spring up here and there alongside the sea, where the people spend lifetimes staring out over the sea, seeing nothing beyond their own dim days ahead. But then no one sees the waves as a surfer sees them. It wasn't long before I did find what I was looking for; the farther north I traveled away from Miami the larger they got, and although the waves never did get as big or as beautiful as Malibu's I had them all to myself.

On weekends I had to call in to the field office every three hours and of course the best surf was always half an hour from the nearest telephone. But I had a ball. I was the only surfer in all of Florida. And for a little while at least I was able to forget all about the FBI.

My lone safaris ranged all the way from Miami to Daytona Beach, more than two hundred miles to the north. And since many of the better spots were so far away I always carried my sleeping bag wherever I went. Many a Friday and Saturday night I spent camped on little out-of-the-way beaches along Florida's eastern coast. Indiatlantic Beach, near Melbourne, was one of my favorites. I camped there just once. That night the mosquitos were almost unbearable. I awoke the next morning cursing and scratching with an infernal buzzing in my ears I couldn't escape. I rolled up my sleeping bag . . . and the buzzing grew louder and I glanced up just in time to hit the deck as a tiny bi-plane zeroed in on me like a freakishly overgrown mosquito and unleashed a cloud of acrid smoke that covered the entire beach, rendering the surf I'd come for completely invisible. I raced to my Volkswagen, for an instant imagining we were under a lethal gas-attack from Cuba. But then the plane made its final pass; it was obviously a crop-duster. But there was no agriculture along the coast and the whole thing remained a mystery until some weeks later someone told me they dusted Indiatlantic every morning in a vain attempt to keep the mosquito population under control.

I gradually discovered that on a strong ground swell a nice break appeared right there on Miami Beach, opposite the corner of Collins Avenue and Twenty-first Street. Those gentle swells reminded me a lot of Waikiki, of a spot near Diamond Head known to the Hawaiians as "Queen's Surf." But in place of hyacinth and sugar cane this gentle headland reeked of French cologne—and when the bikini-boys came wading out into the surf with the come-hither eyes of perverted sharks I dubbed it "Faggot Head."

But I'll never forget that morning at Cocoa Beach when the sun oozed out of the sea like an over-ripe persimmon and I lay there in my sleeping bag breathless, just watching as wave after perfect wave arose glassy and green and then crumbled into golden froth, drenched by the rising sun. In the distance I could barely make out one of the launch towers at Cape Kennedy, dancing in the sunlight. Already the air was heavy and warm. My Malibu buddies would never have believed it—warm water, beautiful waves, and not a soul in sight. A surfer's dream. And to think that only a few months before I'd considered Florida a waveless wasteland.

I rolled up the bag and grabbed my board. The water lapped up around my ankles and I laughed. At home now the temperature would be in the fifties; here it was the same as the air, in the mid-seventies. A big wave crashed. I squinted into the sun. And I froze. A dark shape clung to the glassy shoulder of that wave, then vanished behind it in an instant. Another surfer? Impossible. For the moment I'd been blinded, squinting into the sun like that. Probably a pelican, I thought. They often skimmed over the surf like that looking for fish.

Suddenly another wave rose, shimmering higher than the one before. The sun was behind it—but this time I was sure as the dark shape slid down into the heart of the wave, the dark shape that was a surfer running trim and swift as the wave yawned, then flicking over the crest an instant before it crashed. I stood staring until the white water from his wave rushed about my ankles. I launched into the backwash.

He was a good surfer, tall and wiry with the long soft muscles of a long distance swimmer. But this was my kind of surf and I could handle it pretty well myself. And for the next few hours the two of us—the only surfers in all of Florida —rode wave after sparkling wave within only a few yards of each other without speaking a single word. But then surfing is like that. A lonely sport whose peculiar mystique has often been likened to that of the bull ring, where the conflict is one that may not be shared by any two men.

Finally he took a vicious wipeout and his board went fluttering to shore, coming to rest only a few yards from where I'd just completed a long ride. I paddled it back out to him.

"Thanks a lot," he mumbled awkwardly. "Guess I slipped."

Those were the only words spoken between us in the water. We were both pretty well involved in picking and riding only the best waves that rolled in, though once or twice I did catch him watching me. He always looked away quickly. And every time I paddled down into a wave I could feel his eyes boring into my back. When I suddenly realized it was time to check in with the office I paddled to shore and strapped my board to the car before it was even dry. I didn't want to be late.

I was just brushing the sand from my feet when I heard him walk up behind me. "Well . . . now there's two of us," he said loudly, as if to introduce himself.

I turned and stared up into the bony face of the hard angular man . . . but now on dry land he looked much taller.

We stared at each other for a long minute. His hair was the color of dirty salt water. Probably blond when it's dry, I thought to myself. A typical surfer. Or at least he looked the part even though he seemed a little old for that irresponsible kind of life. He was about my age.

After a long silence and as I was about to step into my car he cleared his throat and said, "Before long there'll be a flock of surfers along this coast." He grinned, revealing a set of buck teeth and continued, affecting a tone of mock tragedy. "The world's too small a place for the likes of me . . . but I guess we might as well be friends." He said it like he was doing me a big favor.

"The name's Jack Murphy, but they call me 'Murph the Surf.' " I introduced myself rather reluctantly as we shook hands and I wondered who else was around to call him that.

"You from California?" he asked.

"Right. . . ."

"Me, too," he interjected, apparently used to having things to himself. Whatever the reason, he seemed to enjoy one-sided conversations. He had a pretty good opinion of himself, too. And it turned out we were *not* the only surfers in all of Florida. There were two others, only Murphy expressed it differently. "A couple of guys up at Daytona have surfboards . . . but when you see 'em in the water you'll know they aren't surfers." He winked knowingly.

Murph the Surf probably would have rambled on for quite some time but I had to get to a phone and I cut him short. We shook hands and I figured I'd probably never see him again.

The next weekend a huge storm blew in and stood stationary off the coast. The paper reported huge waves would soon be battering the coast. But I was busy and couldn't get free until late Saturday afternoon. I knew *Faggot Head* would be breaking and I drove straight there. The sky was grey and I could hear the solid thump of the big storm waves even before I got there. I pulled into the parking lot and watched for awhile, trying to decide just where the waves were best.

The air had turned suddenly cool and most of the bikini set had departed early. I was thankful for that. But the lifeguard wouldn't have let them near the water anyway. The surf was much too angry. Only a gay handful of the regulars remained, huddled together down by the water, bundled up in terrycloth robes and hiding behind sunglasses even though it was overcast.

Suddenly I heard a yell from their direction and I turned to find them staring unmistakably at me. I figured it was the surfboard that excited them and looked the other way. But in the next instant one of them, a spidery fellow in a bright crimson robe, came loping across the sand like a comic gazelle straight for me. I moved to roll up the window but that seemed silly. I looked around frantically. There coming around the corner on a three-wheeled motor scooter was a traffic cop! I started to yell but the words died in my throat as the gazelle called me by name.

"Hey, Ollestad . . . surf's up!"

I just stared as he loomed closer and closer. Then he was grinning down at me. Seeing I hadn't recognized him, he leaned forward and glanced both ways before whispering "Hey, Agent Zero—it's me, Murph!" Still grinning, Murphy removed his dark glasses and revealed his angular profile.

I was dumbfounded. Nobody, not even my landlord knew I was with the Bureau. "Murphy how the hell did you . . . ?"

"Easy, Ollestad, I got contacts." He twirled the glasses

casually between thumb and forefinger. "But hey—where you been? I've been waiting for you here all day."

"What made you think I'd come here?"

"Oh . . . I've learned lots of interesting things about you this week. If you're interested I could. . . ."

"No, thanks, Murph. Think I'll go out and catch some waves." I stepped out of the car and began untying my board. Murphy glanced toward his friends. They were still staring.

"Good idea, Ollestad. I'll join you. I haven't got my board . . . but I can scrounge up a paddleboard somewhere. And afterwards we can join my friends for a drink."

"I'll pass."

"What's the matter?" he laughed. "My friends not good enough for you? They could tell you a lot about this town."

"I'll bet they could, but I'm not sure I want to hear it. Thanks anyway, but I'm busy tonight."

"No you're not. Hey, listen. These cats are interesting. Sure, I know they're a little faggy, but live and let live I always say. They've got an act over at the Thunderbird Hotel where I work. . . ."

"You work?"

"Sure, I teach swimming. And I've got a high-dive act I do there on weekends. But listen—these guys have got an act that's unreal. You'd really dig it. One of them's a female-impersonator and she . . . I mean *he* does a dance called the 'dance of the seven veils,' and when she . . . he gets down to the last veil . . . well, you gotta see it to believe it!"

Even out in the water Murphy maintained the same line of chatter. I even tried insulting him, but nothing seemed to stop him. He just kept on reminding me we were the only two surfers in the state and we had to stick together.

But the waves were terrible (they peaked up and broke much too fast and the rides were disappointingly short) and I ended up just listening to Murphy. Something, possibly the exercise, had loosened me up. I was more relaxed and I gradually began to see him in a new light.

He was harmless enough, and actually reminded me a lot of the surf-nuts at home. After the edge of his first impression wore off his hilarious sense of humor began to grow on me. Apart from his job at the hotel he spent most of his time island-hopping in the Caribbean, skin-diving and chasing the girls from one vacation *spa* to the next. The woods were full of them, but heiresses and secretaries—they were all the same to Murphy. And when one of them left him in the lurch or he ran out of money he'd just sit down and weave hats for the tourists out of palm fronds. When he'd made enough money he'd move on. At least that's how Murphy told the tale.

"You call that work?" I laughed as we climbed back in the car and turned on the heater full blast. I hadn't really meant it as a question, but he took me seriously.

Murphy was shivering so hard he could hardly talk. His lanky frame hadn't much protection against the cold. "Well, Ollestad, if you want to know the truth of it—no. But what did work ever get anybody, besides a big fat ulcer? Answer me that."

I didn't say anything and Murphy applied a towel vigorously to his sandy hair and I thought the subject would die a natural death, but no. "This place is full of working slobs," he said abruptly, gesturing toward a long black Cadillac that was pulling into the parking area a little way down from us. Its windows were rolled up tight. Murphy continued drying his hair and I stared as a youngish girl with flowing bleached-blond hair snuggled at the side of a balding executive-type easily twice her age. Murphy grinned as they both took a long pull from a silver flask.

"Guys like him fly down here with their secretaries—hundreds of them every week, all fat and sloppy. Those are your workers, Ollestad. They're obsessed with work. Cheating on their wives is the biggest adventure in their narrow lives . . . and even then they don't know what to do with themselves unless they're half drunk. Booze takes the edge off of life for them so they don't have to feel anything. They come down here where the sun is hot and the ocean is beautiful and they're afraid to come out of their air-conditioned, rental Cadillacs to sit on the beach and look at the palm trees.

"They're caught up in a giant twister and they can't get out of it and pretty soon they don't even want to get out because they don't know anything else but work. And money. And these little 'business-trips' away from the wife that'll give 'em something to talk about with the boys for the rest of the year. Even when they do see out of their closed-in little worlds they're afraid to move. I've met all sorts of so-called successful businessmen who'd have given anything to have been able to sail away with me out into the Bahamas like I can any time I feel like it. But they're not used to that. It's not part of the pattern and that bugs them. Why don't they at least have the guts to try and break the cycle and get up early in the morning just once and watch the sun come up? The minute it rains they think they've got to run for the nearest bar. What I can't figure out is why don't they do something like they really mean it—like getting into a good fight or grabbing one of the B-girls and dragging her out into the sand dunes for a good tumble . . . or like getting themselves arrested and spending a night in jail for having too good a time *just once in their pathetic little lives!"*

Murphy's eyes were wild and he was shaking and it wasn't all from being cold. He stared at me like he expected an answer.

"I don't know, Murph," I said avoiding his eyes.

"Don't know what?"

"I just don't know. Period. Come on, let's go back to my place and get something to eat."

Little by little I came to like Jack Murphy and we became friends, mostly because we were both surfers but also because we stayed out of each other's private life. Once Murph mentioned he'd been arrested by the Bureau on a bum-check charge, and the way he told the story it sounded like a hilarious adventure. Anything was funny the way he told it —and I laughed, but Murph must have sensed the uneasiness behind my laughter. Our friendship was strained for a few weeks after that, until we both forgot about it, and he never mentioned it again. I was an FBI agent and Murph was a surf-bum. That's the way things stayed.

Murph the Surf knew everyone in Miami, from the groundlings up. He moved freely through that faintly athletic but parasitic culture of bronze insects that inhabits resort hotels from St. Moritz to Waikiki. And Murph rode just as easily in the wake of opulence. Yes, we had some wild adventures, Murph the Surf and I, and many times over he proved his friendship. Every Friday night he'd phone me at his own expense—from Daytona or Melbourne or wherever he happened to call home at the moment—just to let me know how the surf was. He borrowed money occasionally, but never failed to pay it back. And when I ran short, he never refused me, even if it cut his own supply in half. We were friends. But ironically there was another bond between us. The FBI.

After six months in the field special agents were required to retain at least two criminal or potential criminal informants (CI's or PCI's), and the knowledge of Murph's contacts with the Miami underworld always lurked in the back of my mind. The beach boys and cocktail waitresses and the regular habitues of Miami Beach knew all, saw all and said nothing . . . except to Murph the Surf. And to me, because I was Murph's friend. Of course they hadn't the slightest suspicion I was the Bureau. I didn't abuse their confidence for in truth I had no use for their information in my own case-work, but it did amuse me to know what was going on weeks ahead of the agent (SA Darrell Pruett) assigned as liaison to the Miami hotel security offices.

One Saturday afternoon, when the wind was howling and the surf was a mad scramble of whitecaps, I agreed to meet Murph over at his place, which at the moment happened to be the Shoremeade hotel. He was waiting for me in the lobby when I arrived.

"Hello, Murph," I said cheerfully.

Without cracking a smile my angular companion drew a bony finger to his lips and pulled me aside. "Pruett's upstairs with the security boys," he whispered and then broke into an obscene grin as I did a quick double-take. "What's the matter?" he said teasing. "Pruett. You do know the man, don't you?"

I had to laugh. Pruett above all other agents in the Miami field office, always considered himself the sly one. He had everybody buffaloed, even Fife and Alderton. My first instinct was to tell the man at the first opportunity, but by this time I knew it would have done more harm than good. Even when Murph added that all of Miami Beach was wise to Pruett and his informants I kept my silence.

Murphy led me to an empty store-room where he'd taken up house-keeping for the last week. The room was scattered with junk, not the least of which was a pile of palm-fronds at least seven feet high.

"The place smells like a hay-loft, Murph."

"Yeh, but it's worth it, Ollestad. Sit down while I weave up a couple of bucks."

This was Murph's big hat-selling season. The tourists loved them. I pulled up a wooden crate and watched for the next hour as Murph wove hat after hat, his deft fingers flying over the fronds much as they must have on the strings of the violin he'd played as a child prodigy with the Pittsburgh. symphony. Of course that was a long time before, in his "other life," as he used to call it. But Murphy's musical genius never ceased to amaze me. He could pick up most any instrument and play it with ease . . . as I was to learn that very evening.

After dinner at an inexpensive restaurant around the corner from the Shoremeade, Murphy suggested that we take in a movie, and I agreed. But he suddenly recalled making a date with a girl to meet him at the hotel bar, so we stopped by there first. The bar wasn't crowded, a handful of customers mulled over their drinks in a dimly lighted corner. They turned and stared when the bartender hailed Murphy loudly.

"Looks like you got stood up again, Lover-boy," he jeered. "She just left."

"Can't understand it," Murphy lamented, "I'm only an hour late."

"Come on over," the bartender laughed, "and I'll buy you a drink . . . out of sympathy."

Murphy turned to me and shrugged. "That's *Sour-Puss,*" he explained loudly, gesturing to the smiling bartender as we approached the bar. "We call him that because he got thrown out of bartender's school for forgetting to put the sugar in his whiskey sours. . . ."

The bartender laughed appreciatively and together he and my companion launched into the game of barroom insults which I'd learned occupied a good percentage of his leisure time.

The game ended when some customers sat down at the bar and we got up to leave. "Maybe we'll hit you later," said Murphy. "How late's the band gonna stay tonight?"

The bartender shook his head. "No band, Murph. They quit on us last night. . . ."

Murph looked shocked and saddened. "No band? You gotta be kidding." He said it as if such a thing were unthinkable.

"Serious. It's the season, Murph. All the other groups are booked solid. . . ."

Without flinching Murph turned to me and jabbed me with his elbow under the counter. "Did you hear the man? The place needs entertainment . . . I guess we better tell 'em, Ollestad." I was completely puzzled.

Murph leaned across the bar and whispered as if he didn't want anybody else to hear. "Okay, Sour-Puss, I'm gonna let you in on the secret of the year. You just happen to be lookin' at the best guitar and ukulele combo this side of Waikiki. . . . Murph the Surf and Ollestad here, who's better known as *Malibu Mo'kini!*"

I'll never know how it happened, but the next thing I knew it was close to midnight and Murph was hauling me back out onto the dance floor for our fourth chorus of *Ukulele Lady.* Word about our act had spread up and down Miami Beach and now a well-oiled audience of what seemed like at least a thousand stomping tourists were yelling for an encore. Poor Sour-Puss was going nuts trying to concoct the potpourri of Polynesian drinks his customers were ordering in honor of the evening. But Murphy was ecstatic. He held a captive audience, he had all the free booze he could drink, and he'd sold all his hats.

As we finished our second chorus of *Aloha Oye* I noticed a photographer trying to push his way through the crowd and I quickly snapped two strings on my uke and bowed out before he could get any pictures. That's all I'd need. I could see the headlines in the entertainment section of the *Miami Herald*—"Bad-Check Artist and FBI Agent Form Combo." Fife would have had a heart-attack.

I retreated to our table in the darkest corner of the bar. Murphy followed, only slightly bewildered, and instantly fell to the herculean task of consuming all the drinks that had been sent to our table during our final chorus.

He was just getting warmed up when suddenly there came a loud thud and the crowd hushed and the sea of heads turned toward the door where two of the hotel's strong men were trying to wrestle somebody out the door. Quick as a cat Murphy was right in the middle of it.

"Wait a minute!" he commanded. "What's going on here?" he shouted and just as he did the two muscle-men seemed to explode in mid-air, leaving their victim, a freckle-faced kid with the body of a bull ape standing there alone, staring down at them, looking more surprised than anyone.

"Ah just came in fo' a Coca-Cola," he whined comically, and reached down for a battered leather suitcase that he'd apparently brought in with him.

Only Murphy laughed. "Well, come on over to my table. I'll get you a Coke. Hey, Sour-Puss. . . ."

"He can't come in, Murphy," the bar-keep growled. "He's under-age."

"Under-age my ass. I've known this fellow all my life. He's older than you are." Murphy stumbled across to the kid and threw an arm limply about his shoulder. From the way he walked I could tell he was pretty tight.

A demonic smile crossed my partner's face. "What's your name, kid?" he asked.

The kid didn't know what to do and it took him a moment to answer. "William. William Heartly," he said shyly.

Murphy whipped around and held up his arms, demanding the crowd's attention. "All right you people," he yelled, "my old buddy Billy Heartly has come to town to join the Marines and kick ol' Castro's ass out of Cuba . . . and some people don't think he's old enough to buy a Coke! Whadda you think about that?"

The crowd cheered and lunged forward and Sour-Puss and his bouncers were lost in the shuffle as Murphy and a burly fellow ferried the young giant to our table on their shoulders. Someone else brought the suitcase. The kid was seated and Murphy crossed back to the bar and played the diplomat with Sour-Puss for a few minutes and then returned bearing a king-sized Coke and a glass of ice. "Compliments of the house," he said professionally and slumped down into his chair. "Well, now, Bill. Tell us about yourself."

Murphy really played it to the hilt, hanging on the kid's every word and yelling across to the bar every time his glass was empty. Indeed, Billy Heartly *was* under-age, only nine-teen, and he hailed from Fitzgerald, Georgia, where he had been a "swamper," unloading trucks on the docks. That's what had turned him into such a giant. I smiled to myself, remembering Big Z's lecture back at the Quantico Academy about "four-hundred-pound stevedores." That hadn't been so long ago, really, though it seemed like a million years.

The evening wore on and Murphy got tighter. The kid seemed perfectly happy drinking his Cokes, but when he told Murphy that he'd been working for more than a year just saving up for one big Miami vacation I could tell that it hit him wrong. But a moment later he took me by complete surprise and wobbled to his feet and announced that it was Billy Heartly's twenty-first birthday and he led the whole bar in a rousing chorus of happy birthday. Of course it wasn't his birthday and Billy felt badly about it, but he just blushed and stared down at his huge hands. After his first drink, though, Billy Heartly was a tiger. Murphy introduced him to every girl in the place and they loved him. He was a good looking kid anyway. But he had already become a war hero . . . and it was his birthday to boot. He couldn't lose.

It was close to two in the morning when the crowd began to thin. The drinks stopped coming and Murphy began to sober up and I figured he'd let the kid alone. But he didn't. He started ordering more drinks from the bar, paying for them out of his own hat-money. Then I noticed that Murphy wasn't drinking them—the kid was. Or rather Murphy was feeding them to him, one right after another. Billy's eyes were glazed and his girl friends had long since departed.

Murphy leaned forward to light a cigaret and in the flare from the match I saw that he wore the same diabolical expression that he'd worn when the kid first walked into the bar. I'd had just about enough. There was no point in getting the kid drunk. It didn't make any sense. Murphy was doing it out of damn meanness. Besides, I hadn't had anything to drink and the whole evening had begun to drag by like a dull movie. I could hardly keep my eyes open.

"Murphy," I announced crossly, "it's time to leave."

"Just fifteen minutes, Norm," he said pulling me back to my seat. "We gotta close the place down. It's Billy's birthday. . . ." He turned back to the kid, punching him playfully on the shoulder. "Ain't that right, Billy?" The kid lurched toward Murphy and shook his head up and down, but his eyes wouldn't focus.

"Now Billy," he said softly. "I suspect you really came down here to Miami to find you'self a nice girl that you could settle down with . . . didn't you?" Billy just stared. Murphy slung his arm around the wobbly giant. "Well, now, you see that pretty little girl over by the bar? She's from Georgia. That's right . . . *your* country, and she's nineteen years old, just like you." Billy stared over toward the bar and tried to focus on a pretty girl in a bright red cocktail dress. She looked a lot older than nineteen to me. Billy couldn't see, but he leered lustily in the general direction.

"Tell you what I'm going to do for you," said Murphy. "I just happen to know that girl . . ." Billy's eyes brightened. "Her name is Lucy Gaines. And I also happen to know she's been looking for a handsome Georgia boy just like you." He clapped Billy on the back and winked at me and walked over to the bar and introduced himself to the girl. It was plain that he'd never even met her before.

In less than a minute Murphy returned with the girl on his arm and introduced her—and lo and behold she was from Georgia and her name was Lucy Gaines. She was even prettier than she'd looked across the bar, but her face was so caked with makeup I was sure she couldn't have been a day under thirty. She took her seat gracefully between my two companions and immediately pulled Billy into a sugary but painfully one-sided conversation that sounded like she worked for the Georgia chamber of commerce.

Before long we were the only ones left in the whole bar and Sour-Puss was making an obvious display of cleaning up around us and I signaled Murphy that it was time to leave and that this time I wasn't kidding. At first he was hesitant, and I was about to leave without him. But when Lucy Gaines offered to drive young Billy over to her hotel he jumped to his feet, and a moment later we were on our way out the door.

Outside, the streets were nearly empty, but music was coming from somewhere and Billy was doing a miserable job of singing along with it as Murphy and the girl half carried the staggering giant over to her convertible. Suddenly I remembered I'd left my ukulele in the bar and returned for it while Murphy was still saying his last goodbyes to Billy.

Luckily the front door was still ajar and I walked right in. Apparently the bartender had found it, for my ukulele was on the bar, broken strings and all. I was just leaving for the second time when Sour-Puss caught me at the door.

"Where do you guys get off . . . pulling a stunt like that on an innocent kid?"

It took me a moment to decide whether he was serious or not. He was. For the first time that evening his face was screwed up into a lemonish expression entirely worthy of his name.

"What are you talking about?" I ventured.

"Ah come off it—first you sneak the kid in here, then you get him so bombed he forgets his suitcase . . . and then *her*." The bartender reached behind the bar and slid the suitcase across the floor. "Here . . . I don't want nothing more to do with you guys."

Even before Murphy walked in the door I could hear him laughing. The bartender just scowled and shook his head and retreated behind his bar as Murphy staggered in, laughing so hard the tears were streaming down his face. He could hardly stand.

"What's so funny?" I asked.

He tried to answer but choked on the attempt. In a moment he recovered. "I tell you. . . . I just pulled off the all-time funniest bit, Ollestad. That hay-seed thinks he's found the girl he's gonna marry!"

"I don't get the point, Murph. She seemed nice enough. . . ."

"Oh, come on, Ollestad . . . the FBI taught you better than that. That gal's name wasn't Lucy Gaines, it was Janice Cummings, and she's not from Georgia at all. She's from Brooklyn. Ollestad, Janice's the biggest whore in Miami Beach! That's the funny part. She thinks she's gonna turn an easy trick!"

Suddenly and uncontrollably Murphy again roared with laughter, completely broken up by the idea of the hayseed and the whore. I glanced down at the suitcase and felt the sick feeling in my stomach and I pressed past Murphy for the door. I reached for the handle and the door flew open in my face, almost flattening me, and the laughter died in Murphy's throat as he shrank back against the wall and stared up into the enormous visage of young Billy Heartly.

I figured we were in for trouble. But the kid never even saw us. His eyes fell to the suitcase, he reached down mechanically, picked it up, and walked right out the door as he had entered. There was a long silence, then Murphy heaved a sigh of relief and grinned that obscene grin of his and it was all I could do to keep from slamming into those ugly buck teeth. I'd gotten a good look at the kid's face. Something had sobered him up pretty quick. And he was crying.

# 21

I kept running with Murph the Surf even after I realized what a no-good he was. He knew where to find surf, and we got along together fine. With his shortcomings, he was still not as dangerous to me as two of my fellow F.B.I. agents—Fife the supervisor, and Alderton, his spy. Fife wouldn't get off my tail. He'd call me into his office at least three times a week for questioning and special instructions. What he didn't realize was that my attitude had changed. He hadn't found out yet that I wasn't going to turn out like the Cracker, and Wally; that I wasn't going to buck the system and do a lot of extra work: I had decided to take the safe way out and coast in the Bureau until I retired. I had come to the conclusion that George Keady back in training school hadn't been so stupid in telling us new agents our very first day in the F.B.I. that we could *retire* in twenty years. Fife hadn't discovered that the day I received my surfboard from California I had ceased to be a problem for him. To make things easy for myself, I would now do anything he asked me to. If it hadn't been too late, I would have changed the Albin report in a minute.

As I walked into his office, Fife got up from his desk.

"Come in, Mr. Ollestad, I've got something very important to talk to you about."

He always began my interviews with that statement, but armed with my new rather cavalier attitude, I just played it for laughs. "Oh, yes sir!" I said, and sat down.

"I can't see it Ollestad. I can't see how I can keep you from getting fired. You've been hanging around Spence and Post again. You have your own cases, you're supposed to go out on your own and work them. Self-reliance it's called."

Fife was really getting bad information from Alderton. I hadn't even talked to either Wally or the Cracker for a month. I didn't say anything, so the supervisor went on.

"You've got to develop some PCI's or CI's in the next few weeks. I can't cover for you much longer." Fife's plaintive tone showed he was just worried about covering for himself.

"Well, Mr. Fife," I finally said, "the rule states that an agent must develop at least two potential criminal informants after six months in the field, my time isn't quite up yet. Besides, I can't bring myself to pay a couple of old drunks for information about the latest theft from the Greyhound bus depot just to be able to say I have two PCI's."

Fife could see that he was getting nowhere, so he turned to the Director for help, relied on what J. Edgar always said about the F.B.I.'s informant program. "Norm, a great percentage of our accomplishments can directly be attributed to information received from confidential informants. When you criticize our informant program, you are aligning yourself with other enemies of the Bureau who criticize it, members of the subversive and criminal underworld. The informant program has played a vital role in the national war against lawlessness. John Dillinger was captured and shot because of an informant, a prostitute. That is why the Direc-

tor is pleased when his agents develop prostitutes as informants, they provide some of our best information."

I knew this was partially true. Some of Spence's best bank
robbery informants were prostitutes.

Fife kept on lecturing me. "Communists and others have
often tried to confuse the words 'informant' and 'informer'
in the public mind, in order to bring the honorable, effective
informant system into disrepute." The supervisor smiled,
walked over to his desk, picked up a dictionary. "Let's see
what Webster has to say about this problem. . . . An 'informer' is one who informs against another by way of accusation and complaint, but an informant is one who gives information of whatever sort." Fife put down the dictionary
and continued. " 'Informer' is often, 'informant' is never, a
term of disdain. During a period of 1959 and 1960, informants furnished data in Bureau cases which resulted in . . ."
Fife looked at some figures on his desk. He had given this
little speech before ". . . ah, the arrest of 1,982 persons and
$2,614,565 in recovered stolen property. Information fur-
nished by confidential informants which relates to offenses
not within our jurisdiction and which is promptly dissemi-
nated to the appropriate agencies led to 2,364 arrests and
recoveries of $1,203,932 by other law enforcement agencies.
The hearings of the House Un-American Activities Com-
mittee at Boston, Atlanta, Newark and other cities in 1958
showed the desperate need of undercover work in fighting
subversive activities.

"At periodic intervals the reliability and integrity of the
informants is carefully checked, to make certain that they
are maintaining acceptable procedures, furnishing reliable
information and are measuring up to the standards that the
public has a right to expect of the F.B.I."

"Okay, okay, I'll go get some informants," I said.

Then Fife let me go.

I fully planned to enlist a couple of the derelicts who hung out over on Flagler Street in downtown Miami. They were safe enough, and the supervisor would have readily approved them. But to sign them up involved a little work and "besides," I told myself, "they would never produce a single bit of worthwhile information."

Additionally, Jack Murphy knew the beach boys, bell hops and waitresses on Miami Beach, and there was nothing that occurred on the beach side without their knowing about it.

And Murph the Surf threw a red hot informant right into my lap. We were lying on the sand one warm Saturday morning on the beach in front of the Thunderbird Hotel. I had been up all night the night before on a surveillance at the Miami airport and was trying to get some sleep and catch up on my tan at the same time. Apparently Murphy had slept all night, because he was as lively and talkative as a myna bird and wouldn't leave me alone.

"Ollestad, just look at all these beautiful women out here on the beach! Have you ever seen so much talent in one place at one time? How can you lie there and sleep like a dullard when there is so much to be done, so many worlds to conquer?"

I rolled over from my stomach to my back. "Lay off, Jack, I'm trying to get some sleep." But Murphy wouldn't stop.

"Ollestad, is there anything I can get you, sir, a bottle of beer—an Alka Seltzer, or some seltzer water—for 2¢ plain...?"

Murphy stood up, put his hands on his hips in an affected manner and gazed up and down the beach. "Mr. Ollestad, how about one of these young ladies for a present? You can just pick out any of the young ladies you would like to have a date with on this beach and I'll arrange it for you, *monsieur.*"

"For Christ's sake, Jack, cut it out," I said, but I had one eye open by this time.

"I mean it—I mean it, Ollestad, you pick the best looking girl on this beach and I'll fix it up for you."

So to get Murph off my back I nodded towards a girl that I had already picked out before I lay down to nap, a short girl with brown hair, brown eyes, a very good figure and wearing a bikini. "Over there," and I pointed to the girl, as I rolled over on my stomach again. I expected it would take Murphy a few minutes to attempt to deliver.

Murphy burst out in a roaring laughter, and exaggerated his mirth by rolling over and over in the sand. "God, is that funny," he said. "That's Judy, she works right at the Thunderbird from noon to 6:00—she and I are old friends."

So I made the scene with Judy Cova. After I took her out a few times, I found out that her father, Harry Cova, owned an interest in some of the Miami Beach hotels. I also found out that he was a goody buddy of Meyer Lansky, one of the top hoods in the United States, and also knew "Butch the Fat," a smaller type gangster. We had three dossiers on Harry Cova in the security files in the Miami field office, and who knows how many reports back at the Seat of Government.

A lot of F.B.I. agents worked a long time and tapped a lot of telephone wires to get all that information. I could have gotten more, but it would have been too dangerous. If something had gone wrong I might have been fired, so I kept my relationship with Judy light and entertaining and didn't dig for information. Judy was quite a girl. A sophomore at the University of Miami, and only 19, she was the raw material out of which would come the gracious, beautiful woman she would some day be.

She had straight well groomed brown hair which flipped up at the ends—the flip of that curl always bounced slightly whenever she laughed or looked up at me. She was perennially tanned—her olive skin and athletic figure wore it nicely. It always bugged me that she knew Murphy, and that her dad was a hood. But her deep brown eyes were innocence personified. She seemed so unaware of her father's wrongdoing, and she was so naive about the world outside of the university. But she tried. Doggedly and earnestly she read and studied, and with an innocent lack of sophistication she would attempt to drag me into political discussions to show me how intelligent and worldly she was. I'd never enter into the political talk. I didn't know anything about it and neither did she.

I taught her how to surf, and she brought back some of my old enthusiasm. I started playing the guitar again—regularly, just like a serious hobby, and we went to all kinds of concerts. We'd park at the beach in my Volkswagen and then just talk for hours.

It's strange about girls. If they're snobbish, sloppy, or loud . . . or ugly, you can't stand 'em even if their father is the President of the United States. But if you think that maybe there is a chance you might fall in love someday, it doesn't matter if her father is a gangster.

Judy and I never got quite that far. The famous one-two punch of the F.B.I. in Miami—Fife and Alderton—got to me first. I knew I was in trouble when Fife called me into his office one evening after work and read me the riot act.

"Ollestad, this is absolutely the end. I am at the end of the rope. The security squad has a continuous surveillance on one of the local hoodlums in the area—a fellow by the name of Cova. You know, we take down the auto license numbers of all the people who park in front of Cova's house." Fife deliberately paused and dramatically stomped around his desk like a giant, fat rooster. "And what did we find last Tuesday night? None other than Special Agent Norman T. Ollestad's Volkswagen, parked out in front of the Cova house and for 2½ hours. The license check just came in today— here's the report!" He threw a 302 report at me.

"What the hell were you doing, parked out in front of Cova's house with his daughter in the car?" Fife thundered.

"What the hell do you THINK I was doing?" I retorted as I picked up the report.

Supervisor Fife puffed himself up and leaned casually against one corner of his desk. "Now, wait a minute Ollestad, just wait a minute. You think I'm a square, huh? Don't you? I happen to know something about the facts of life . . . and it's physically impossible in a Volkswagen. Besides, two and a half hours . . . oh, come now Ollestad." A wry smile crept up between Fife's two fat cheeks and he looked up toward the ceiling for a moment. Then all of a sudden he snapped back to me and continued. ". . . and in addition, Special Agent Eaton Alderton, through a sutech, has discovered that you called the Cova residence in Hollywood Florida every night last week."

"You don't have to use that polite language, Mr. Fife," I said. "Sutech—I know what a sutech is—Alderton has tapped my phone and he has been listening to my telephone conversations."

"That's right, Ollestad, and you're in trouble."

But I had learned how to protect myself against the likes of Fife and Alderton. I smiled and leaned back and tried not to show my nervousness as I attempted a defensive ploy.

"Well, if Alderton has been tapping my phone then he should know what I'm working on. The last time I was in here you told me you desperately needed criminal informants, so I decided to go out and do something about it."

I looked at Fife hopefully to see whether or not he was buying my story. It was working.

"So," I continued, "I have now signed up two of the hottest informants in southern Florida—a fellow, Jack Rolland Murphy, known as Murph the Surf, and Judy Cova, the daughter of one of the top ten hoodlums."

Fife was wary. "Why the hell haven't you been telling us about it, Ollestad; you are supposed to be working for the F.B.I.—you're supposed to let us know about these things."

"Well," I answered, "I haven't uncovered any information yet, didn't have anything to tell you."

The supervisor wasn't as sure of himself as he had been at the beginning of the interview—he began to ask worried questions.

"What makes you think you're going to find out anything just taking out Cova's daughter?"

"Well, Mr. Fife," I challenged, "you've been in this business a lot longer than I have. You know that the security squads of the F.B.I. all over the United States are working like beavers all the time to get any little thing they can." I had heard about the F.B.I. agents in Las Vegas who had planted a microphone and transmitting device in Chicago gangster Sam Giancana's bedroom. They hadn't gotten much hard information, but they did get a good recording of Sam with a member of a famous sisters' singing trio. That "wild bedroom scene" made the rounds of the F.B.I.'s 57 field offices in a hurry. "I can save the other agents on the security squad a lot of work and sweat," I continued, "like when Wayne Wintrode dressed up as a carpenter and put that mike in the plastered wall of Butch-the-Fats' new home out on North Miami Beach. I can place a microphone the easy way."

"Your trouble, Ollestad," Fife concluded, "is that you are always trying to do everything by yourself and you think you're too damn smart. Now go right down to the security squad and see Wayne Wintrode, who is supposed to be in charge of all sutech's, by the way, and he'll tell you how to work this case properly."

I was dismissed, I had survived the Fife-Alderton purge and come out on top, but I had also stuck my neck out. It was dangerous working with high-powered informants. Judy Cova's father was enough of a risk, but in anything but surfing, Murph the Surf was, to say the least, undependable.

Wintrode, the wire-tap man, was overjoyed. He immediately set out on a plan. I was to wangle a dinner invitation from Judy, and then plant a microphone inside Harry Cova's home. I talked him out of it.

"Jesus, Winnie," I pleaded, "the old man is liable to search me the first time I show up at his house, he's no dummy."

So my supervisor settled on an alternative plan. I was to go into the home for dinner and during the course of the evening, use the bathroom and stop up the plumbing in some way. When old man Cova called the plumber the security squad would, through the use of a telephone tap, determine which plumber was assigned to the job. Then they would arrange to have one of our own men dressed as a plumber come out to the Cova house, and in the process of fixing the pipes the agent was to plant a bug, a transmitting device, in the bathroom. It was a brilliant plan. The only thing we ever got out of that recording device was hours of recording tapes of running water, flushed toilets and an occasional emission of gas.

So with my back to the wall I talked Judy into inviting me over to her house.

The night of the dinner arrived. Indeed, the old man would have taken a dim view of having an FBI agent to dinner, but the whole family thought I taught swimming over at the beach. I was safe for the moment—but Judy had also invited Murph the Surf, who was just liable to say or do anything.

I drove up and parked before the large, sprawling white stucco and marble home, and Judy's mother answered the door. She ushered me inside with the poise of a *grande dame,* incongruous to the household image I had of Harry Cova. Before me stood the beautiful and womanly image of what Judy would become in a few years. Unlike Judy, though, her face was not radiant with enthusiasm, and before the evening was finished I would glimpse behind that beautiful, cultured being, and into the grim pathos surrounding her life with Harry Cova.

She saw me to a chair and spoke in soft, husky tones. "Mr. Ollestad, it's so nice to meet you. Judy will be with us in a moment. . . ." Before she had a chance to speak further, the huge and sinister frame of Cova loomed before me.

He was friendly, but coarse. He immediately plunked a bottle of the best Scotch in my hand, insisting that it was my gift for the evening, and I should take it home with me. He led me through a brisk one-sided conversation that touched on boxing, baseball and the horse-races. The four-letter words flew thick and fast; he bragged constantly, and when I did manage to get a word in edgewise, he sat surrounded by a nimbus of cigar smoke and appraised me with an icy stare, obviously trying to see inside the guy his daughter had been spending so much time with.

We had steak for dinner—Cova cooked it himself. Wouldn't let the cooks touch it. He took our orders, cooked the meat, and yelled at the maid when she tried to help him serve it. After dinner we had a few drinks . . . and then Murphy decided to have a little fun. "Say, Mr. Cova, how are you getting along with the FBI?" I couldn't believe my ears.

If Cova was shocked he didn't show it. He laughed loudly. "How the hell would I know, Jack? But let me tell you somethin' funny. I saw old J. Edgar the other day, out at Hialeah race track. . . ."

"No kidding?" Murph said, winking at me. The bastard.

"Yeh. Christman, the number-two man, came over to my box and told me *the Chief*—that's what he said—*the Chief* wanted to see me. I told him fine . . . but he'd have to come over to where I was, because I don't move for nobody—and that means nobody—when they're runnin'!"

"Is that right?" said Murph. He was egging Cova on.

"Sure. And a little later he brings the old man over and introduces us—he's gettin' fatter than hell!" Cova thumped himself in the gut to show us all how solid he was, and then continued. "So Hoover asks me for the winning numbers—right there in the Turf Club! The nerve of that guy. I'm just meetin' him for the first time and he comes right out and asks me for the winning numbers. . . ."

"So you gave him the winners?" Murph asked.

"Hell no!" Cova exploded. "I didn't give him nothin'. Wouldn't give him the sweat off my ————. That guy's got a lotta nerve."

I figured this was a good time to feign some sort of emergency and go to the bathroom. It was easy because I really was beginning to feel a little queasy. Cova showed me to the bathroom, I locked myself in and clogged the toilet as best

I could. When I came out I was more relaxed, having done all I could for the FBI that night.

I noticed that Judy looked more beautiful than ever that evening, in a snug black dress, black heels, and a single strand of pearls around her neck. We all actually enjoyed ourselves for the rest of the evening. Murphy never did reveal my secret, at least as long as I knew Judy he didn't, but the possibility was always in the back of my mind.

When it was about time to leave, Cova pulled Judy and me aside. "Now lookit, young fellah," he said. "Judy's mother and I have noticed that you're one of the finest young men who's come around..." Judy colored with embarrassment. "And Judy's mother is a very perceptive woman . . . *very perceptive*. And I can vouch for that, son. Well, anyway, we've both noticed you've spent quite a wad of money lately, taking Judy out to dinner and all. And we want you to have this!" He rammed a bill into my palm, then clasped it, dwarfing my hand with his thick, but well manicured paw. "We want you to have this so you'll be able to treat our daughter in the style which she's accustomed to."

I had no choice but to accept a fifty dollar bill from the very man whom I had just set up for a F.B.I. sutech.

Judy knew something had gone wrong in my first visit to her home—she knew it was all over. Later that night when I kissed her she had tears in her eyes. I suppose she'll always think it was the fifty dollars her crass, officious father gave me, or something about her that was wrong, but it was the F.B.I. sutech.

We went out a few times after that dinner at her house; she was a very attractive girl and I'd call her if I needed a nice good looking date for show . . . but it was impossible for us. . . . I could just see Fife and Hoover approving the marriage.

# 22

But while I faded with Judy, I was making a big hit with Fife. I worked my automobile theft cases religiously and did all the paper work with precision. It only took about four hours a day to keep right on top of it. The rest of the time I would sit around the office and gas with some of the older agents.

One of the more interesting old timers was Special Agent Joseph R. Laird. I loved to chide him, get him all worked up about something. He was on the security squad, but he only worked Communists—that is, when he worked. Most of the time he would sit around and talk; he liked to argue. Once I asked him if I could get on his squad. It usually made him mad if a young green-horn asked to be let on his precious Commie squad, but he was very civil to me that day

"What are the chances of getting on your Commie squad for a few weeks, just to learn the ropes?" I queried.

As Laird began talking, he instinctively looked around the room for Fife and Alderton. They weren't present. "I'll save you the trouble," he replied. "I'll *tell* you the 'ropes' without wearing out the seat of your pants attending meetings. I've been on the squad for five years here and ten in New York. The CPUSA is dead if the Boss would let it pass. It is socially, financially, politically dead. Membership has plummeted from 80,000 to the present 7,000. Even the old German 'Bund' had more—8,300 in 1937; and the Ku Klux Klan had 6 million members in 1925."

"What have you been doing the last 15 years then?" I challenged.

"Listen, God dammit, we have to keep close tabs on the espionage activities of the USSR and satellites, and China. That's a big job, and we're handling them, too. But that will always be a problem as long as the Bureau's in charge of maintaining security in the U.S. Hell, those Israeli agents cause us a lot of work here. You've heard of the Sherutai Habitachon—the 'Shinbet.' They're the smallest but best espionage organization in the world—those Israelis. The Cubans, ask Wally about that. But as far as the Commies taking over the U. S. Government from within, forget it. The CPUSA is finished. The only thing that keeps them going is J. Edgar Hoover himself. The F.B.I. gives them the money, and the publicity."

I didn't say anything. I couldn't have cared less about what Laird was saying, but he launched into more examples to back up his point.

"Their newspapers are always in the red, have a smaller circulation than almost any other publication in the U. S. Hell, in Los Angeles alone you could get more than 7,000 to join the John Birch Society, or a nudist colony, or a movement to impeach Warren. The CPUSA is gone I tell you.

"Why do you think the Director has such a large personal following in America? Because of his reputation as a crime fighter? Hell no, crime has increased tremendously here during his career. It's because he has convinced people that he is the only person that stands between them and a Commie take-over in the U. S. It allows him to make comments and speeches about subjects that otherwise would be out of his field. Now he can talk about the Commie movement in the civil rights, the Supreme Court decisions, the Communist speakers on U. S. college campuses, the moral, religious, political undertones of communism. He speaks on foreign affairs. He even commented on the trade agreements with iron curtain countries in the Harvard Business Review the other day, and a possible wheat sale to Russia."

By this time, I wasn't listening too closely to Laird's ramblings. I was a little sorry I'd set him off.

"Have you ever taken a close look at the crumb-bums that lead the CPUSA? They are all living in another age, the depression years when they were of some consequence. They dress, talk and look like the old days. They're all old and sloppy. We're in so easy, I can't blame the Director for not forgetting them. Organized crime is much tougher, much more a menace to the security and well being of Americans, but the big hoods are younger, have more money, brains. I'd rather tackle the CP than the hoods."

"I'm not too sure I'll sleep well tonight, Joe, with you in charge of the nation's security." I laughed at Laird, but he didn't smile back. Laird plowed on like a college professor. He was determined to make his point with me. The poor frustrated old coot, what difference did it make?

"Espionage will always be a major problem for the U.S. as long as the cold war lasts, and should be our major concern. But it hasn't been that way in the FBI. I've spent most of my fifteen years on Security concentrating on the CPUSA's supposed takeover of our government, and protecting *myself* within the Bureau to avoid being fired. So have the other guys on security, and what has happened? The Soviets had over forty high-level agents in various Washington departments and agencies during World War Two, and Russia stole our atomic bomb secrets. The FBI, *us, we* were supposed to guard America against the espionage menace—the

Communist menace; we were put in charge of espionage. The Army's G-2 was merely handling the background investigations of the scientists. We locked the gate after the horse had been stolen. What the hell were we doing before it happened? Filling out number three cards correctly, surviving inspections, dictating reports within the deadlines. Norm, it'll happen again. It'll happen again that the Bureau, one of our fellow special agents will have a chance to alter the course of history by using his initiative, but will fumble the chance because he's afraid not to play it safe."

I knew it wouldn't do any good, but I attempted to shut him off with some information of my own that I'd learned back in training school. "Joe, you're the expert, but I happen to know that the Director has been studying communism, and warning the American people about its dangers since 1918."

To my surprise, Laird agreed with me, but then rambled on further. "He is an astute observer of the commies. I tell you, Ollestad, he's the Master Mountebank, he's organized his Bureau just exactly like the Communist Party U.S.A. is organized, and has used exactly the same principles the commies use, to control us, the rank and file. You've been undergoing indoctrination similar to the experience of a new Communist recruit, and it'll continue throughout your Bureau career." Laird threw his hands over his head in despair. "I'll tell you more sometime."

"Oh no you won't," I thought to myself as I finally was able to walk away from Laird's desk. I vowed never to start him off again, and I never really thought about what he had told me that day until President Kennedy was assassinated in Dallas, Texas. Old Laird's wild speculations might have had some validity.

One of the supervisors that I'd met during training school, a frightened, worry-wart that taught my New Agents' Class was on the desk in the Dallas, Texas field office of the F.B.I. on the day that President Kennedy was killed. The information about the assassin, Lee Harvey Oswald, information that the F.B.I. was supposed to disseminate to the secret service, went across his desk in time to save the president. It's stupid speculation to try to blame one man for such a catastrophe, but I'll never believe that it couldn't have been prevented if an FBI agent like the Georgia Cracker, or Walton Post, had been administratively advanced to Dallas. Instead, it seems that the Fifes and Aldertons provide the leadership of the F.B.I. in a time of crisis.

But back in 1961, I couldn't be concerned with anything Joe Laird had to say. The only thing I had to worry about was the pending field office inspection.

It was nothing at all. The whole Miami office knew about it two days in advance and we were prepared.

All of us agents signed out at 5:15 the night before the goon squad arrived, stayed in the office, and rehearsed the questions and answers on the surprise test that was to be given at the close of the week's inspection.

I had Leo clean and blue my Smith & Wesson, and he insisted on polishing my badge also. I brought all my files and serials up to date myself. I was ready for anything.

Our penance for cheating on the time cards for 51 weeks was the necessity to get up early every morning during the inspection week, and arrive at the office between 6:30 and 7:00 to conform our cards with the rest of the year. I stayed out of everyone's way for four days, but on the fifth received a notice tacked to my number three card to see the inspector at 3:00 P.M. Nervously I walked into the SAC's office at five to three.

"Well, hello there, Mr. Odegaard. I remember you, good to see you again. I'm Special Agent Russel Gibson, from training and inspection at the Seat of Government."

What a phoney Gibson was. He didn't even know my name.

"I guess I won't have much to do with you since you've just come out of our training school and know the rules better than some of these old hands out here in the field. That's why we have them in for a two-week in-service training period every two years, but it's not like new agents' training, by any means. Nothing can substitute for thirteen weeks of new agents' training."

I was an "old hand" myself by now, at least at personal interviews. I immediately appreciated that if Inspector Gibson found my work below par it would be a reflection on the Academy back in Washington rather than the field supervisors in Miami. I knew then that I'd pass inspection.

"What is the procedure for bank robberies?"

"The first agent on the scene is the number one man. He directs the initial investigation, obtains a description of the individuals or individual who committed the robbery, and informs the next agent to arrive, of the escape route. The number one man is personally responsible for the initial investigation. He must. . . ."

"That's enough. What is the policy on the use of Bu autos?"

"The rule is that they are not to be used to transport agents for non-business purposes, such as lunch, dinner, or coffee breaks."

Gibson's eyes shot up quickly from the papers in front of him. "There is no mention of coffee breaks in the handbook. Where did you get that idea? Have you or any other agents here in Miami been going on coffee breaks?"

"No." If the other agents had heard me mention coffee breaks, they'd sure have given me a hard way to go when the inspectors left.

"Come on, now, I'm a reasonable man, and I know that you wouldn't have mentioned coffee if it wasn't on your mind." He looked at me accusingly.

I gave no answer. I was determined to salvage the rest of the interview by observing a golden silence.

Gibson wasn't interested in stirring up a tempest on the next to the last day of the inspection, especially if he really had to work, but he sensed a weakness in me because of my slip about coffee breaks, so he tried a few gambits that had worked on the last inspection in San Juan, Puerto Rico. He needed something to show he was in there digging for the Director every step of the inspection tour, even here at the next to the last office they had stormed. Only the Tampa field office was left after a trip that had taken them to Atlanta, Jacksonville, Mobile, Charlotte, Knoxville, New Orleans, Savannah and Memphis.

He tried to catch me on something that wouldn't reflect my training at the Academy, something that would involve the field office practices in Miami.

"Is there any situation where Bu rules permit the use of a dirty Bureau automobile?" Gibson asked.

I didn't answer "yes" or "no" because of the danger of a direct quote that might be seized upon. I began and ended with the explanation: "On any investigation in the hill country of the south or west United States a clean automobile will be taken by the local populace to be a treasury agent's car, one from the alcohol and tobacco tax division, internal revenue. The rule is, drive a dirty car and avoid rifle and shotgun fire in the hill country."

The inspector didn't appreciate my humor, but the rule stated was basically correct.

"Where is your office of preference?"

"San Juan, Puerto Rico." I answered quickly.

"Oh, you want to get out to California, huh? There are two theories about that. Tell the Director you want to go where you really don't, and he'll send you the farthest away, or where you really want to go—after ten years of course. But every once in awhile," a smile tried to fight its way into Gibson's face, but could only curl up the left corner of his mouth, "he'll give you the office you request, so you'd better watch out son."

Inspector Gibson was considered the bon vivant of the small circle of inspectors he ran with. He got the drunkest every night. This was the pinnacle, but had to be accomplished with a few bottles in the inspectors' motel rooms. A place where they could quietly pass out after each performance. Inspectors were never allowed to play golf, attend the races, go out drinking, or visit friends while on a "tour." But, if you were a liver, a "regular guy," you fulfilled the Bureau man's idea of true celebration. No poker games, no women. But bottled booze, alone, was the thing.

I studied Gibson's face. It looked like a field of pink, puffy marshmallows. It must be a sorry job to be assigned as an inspector, your only recreation a drinking contest every other night and a wish that the other inspectors noticed how much you'd downed so that they would kid you about it the next day.

Whatever feelings I was generating toward the inspector were killed by the tone of his voice as he continued questioning me.

"Okay, let's get down to cases. Your revolver, please."

I pulled it out, snapped open the chambered cylinder, slipped out five rounds, and handed it over. A sparkling blue.

"Your badge."

Leo had been right. Triumphantly, I offered it up—to be promptly taken from its leather cover, its back inspected with care. No dust, no green corrosion on the brass, it was shiny even on the back side. Funny about these badges, I thought as I watched Gibson's inspection. We never use them—always show our credential. Just another thing to get tarnished or lost.

Gibson flipped the badge from hand to hand, then spoke. "These badges are very important, especially down here in the south. Many times you'll have to identify yourself to ignorant niggers and they won't be able to read your credential. You will have to use your badge in that situation. They understand that badge, they know authority—that is, if you know how to use it—you can't give them an inch, the only thing they understand is force. I don't blame them for it, that's all they know, they were descended from slaves. That's all they know."

Gibson wound up my interview with a few quickies.

"Do you have any problems?"

"No."

"The Director takes a personal interest in his agents. If you have any problems, personal or otherwise, let us know and we'll do something about them. Is everyone treating you fairly here in Miami?"

"Yes."

"Do you have any criticism of the way this inspection was conducted?"

"No."

"Do you have any criticism of the way the Director runs the Bureau?"

"No."

"Come now, he is vitally interested, as he has stated many times, in all his agents and realizes that he and the Bureau grow and benefit from the constructive criticism of you, the agents. Are you sure that you are absolutely satisfied with everything in this Bureau?"

"Yes."

The inspector marked another picket on the long list of special agents who had stated they were satisfied.

"You are dismissed."

I passed the inspection unscathed. We all did. The inspectors found only two criticisms, two failings of the Miami field office, which were immediately remedied. Two weeks later the SAC Volney Davis read us the official report of our inspection just issued from the Seat of Government.

"The flag of the United States, posted in the main waiting room was found to be hanging upon an inappropriate standard. Since the United States is not in a state of declared war, the tip of the flag standard should have been covered with an eagle, not with the spear. The spear should only be used at time of war. This condition was immediately remedied by the SAC personally.

"Four telephone books, which were located in the main waiting room accessible to the general public, were found to be in a generally run down condition, having dog eared pages and marked up covers. In some instances, whole pages were missing from the books; pages 4, 5, 42, and 910 of the first, 4, 5, 42, and 960 of the second, 10, 73-6, 92, and 103 of the third, and 3-10, and 107 from the fourth. This condition, which could result in bad public relations for the Bureau, was immediately remedied by the SAC."

Our Special Agent in charge, Volney Davis, beamed as he

finished reading the report. "Well, fellows, we did it again. We passed another inspection. We did it as a team, pulling together."

Then our SAC feigned sadness. "Boys, I hate to tell you this, but I'm being transferred to Oklahoma City next month. I'll trade places with their SAC, Teasely A. Krappman."

Now it was our turn to feign sadness, so we all performed mightily. But some of the old time agents weren't faking it, they were genuinely sorry to get the new SAC.

Krappman swept into Miami with quite a reputation. He had taken personal control and supervision over both the Turner and Gibbons incidents, infamous personnel cases within the Bureau; both Turner and Gibbons had been fired from their jobs as special agents. He had come out on top in both instances, but still had one final hurdle, the civil service hearing involving Turner. If Krappman didn't survive the hearing; in other words, if Turner did, it would mean that Krappman had been wrong or had misled the Director in his handling of the problem, and Krappman would have to be demoted. It became necessary to provide material for Krappman's demise in the event it had to be used in the future.

So Krappman brought something in addition to his reputation—an exclusive F.B.I. phenomenon known as a "surprise inspection."

In direct contrast to its immediate predecessor, this inspection caught all of us unprepared.

I was cruising over the beach to interview the wife of a "master check writer" when the girl on the radio quaked, "MM49, would you please come back to the office immediately, the INSPECTORS want to see your car." The tip was unnecessary: her shaky voice told the story, an "unscheduled" inspection.

I turned a big "U" on the causeway and started back toward the garage. The inspectors had returned eleven months early, and they wouldn't leave until serious violations of Bureau rules were uncovered. I knew that everything would depend on whom they were after, since there was ample evidence to fire the entire office if they wanted to.

Some agents would be discharged, a few suspended or transferred, the lucky ones would just receive personal letters of censure from the Director—but those letters would be different from the ones received at the "regular" inspection. The latter ones were usually balanced with personal letters of commendation within the year to make the recipient eligible for his in-grade pay raises and possible promotions, and doubly grateful to the Director for his beneficence. The censures received at unscheduled inspections would stick for years. In spite of all this confronting me, I wasn't worried a bit. I had carefully covered myself on paper. My voluntary overtime was exactly the same as the office average, my Time in the Office, T.I.O., was very low. I was set.

But I wasn't quite ready for the surprise waiting for me at the F.B.I. garage.

"Mr. Ollestad, I'm Inspector Claude Lightfoot, pleased to see you again. They call me Senator Lightfoot, you can just call me senator." With that the senator smiled a broad benign look, like a southern sheriff just about to apply an electric cattle prod to another fellow human being.

As I set the brake and got out of the car I realized, with an inward gasp of horror, that I knew the senator. He was my fat inspector friend from the F.B.I. Academy at Quantico, Virginia, the head watcher, the man who had been knocked down on the bootball field.

# 23

As two inspectors went over my auto with meticulous care, the senator engaged in conversation.

"Norman Ollestad. I remember you distinctly in training school. Always well groomed, dressed in a conservative businessman's suit. Whatever have they done to you out here in the field? You need a haircut, your suit needs pressing, and those button-down collars are going to get you into trouble. I've never arrested a queer yet that wasn't wearing one of those, and a striped tie. I think that the field office has been a bad influence, don't you?"

I silently assented with a nod of my head, so intimidated I would have agreed to anything.

"Any field office problems can be traced to one man, and one man only, the SAC. Don't you agree? . . . Cat got your tongue, Mr. Ollestad?"

278

I was overjoyed to hear that it was the SAC, Krappman, they were primarily after. The blessing was mixed with the realization that if my own conduct was found to be substandard, it would corroborate the case against Krappman; I was a secondary target. And the senator had recognized me from the Academy.

"Enough of this idle talking, Mr. Ollestad. Let's go over to the office and take a look at your cases. Incidentally, where have you been today?" He continued to smile pleasantly.

"Several places, as indicated by my number three card," I mumbled. I was so scared I was short of breath. The inspector really had me where he wanted me now.

"Your number three card! The card that indicates where you are and what you are doing at all times, right? Maybe we'd better take a look at that card first."

I didn't worry too much about this particular challenge. I was always careful to put leads on the number three that were pertinent. Some of the sloppy agents occasionally listed leads from cases they had already closed; they fell like tenpins at one of these surprise inspections.

For the first two days of the inspection, the senator and I covered every letter, report, file that I had handled, every piece of paper. No violations of the Bureau rules were found. But with the senator on my back, I had other problems.

"Mr. Ollestad, we can tell you what to do back in the Academy, but the SAC and your supervisor must *show* you how to do it, until you get more experience. Has either one gone over your agent handbooks or manual of instructions with you personally since you arrived here at Miami?"

"I think so." I was hedging.

"Agents are positive, they don't guess. If you are called to testify as a witness in court, you can't guess, you're under oath, you must be positive about facts. Isn't that true, Ollestad?"

"Yes." I sensed I was getting in deeper every minute. . . .

"Don't you think that you have lacked adequate supervision here in Miami?"

"I don't think so," I repeated.

"You don't learn very fast, do you Ollestad? After I just told you that agents are never wishy-washy about their facts, you say you 'don't think so'. Speak up, the Director doesn't like his agents to mumble; . . . the ones that are going to be with us for awhile, that is. Maybe that's not too important to you to be with the F.B.I., but suit yourself."

Before I could speak, Lightfoot fired another question. "Name the top four associates to the Director in this Bureau."

"Earl T. Christman is Associate Director. Then there are two assistants to the Director. William Dainard is one of them, but he takes a personal interest and responsibility for training and inspection, which is headed by Jess Doyle, assisted by Frank Nash." I gave a bad answer. The senator picked it up.

"Now Ollestad, we informed you of all the leadership while you were in training school, had you memorize the men I've just asked you about; you were tested. You haven't named them all, which is a giveaway that you have forgotten some of the information. We must have thoroughness, completeness in our agents. Those who cannot retain important facts must be drummed out of our Bureau. But it's hard to completely fault you. It's because of inadequate supervision that you've faltered a little on the path to becoming a real agent. Isn't that right?"

"Yes." I agreed.

"Will you sign a written statement to that effect?" Lightfoot sprang into action, began writing furiously.

He stopped with my answer. "No."

"The Director doesn't like uncooperative agents, or those who lack judgment. The stool-pigeon idea is a product of the underworld. You have an obligation to yourself, to your future in the F.B.I., to put your finger on the real cause of your personal difficulty, the cause of any future trouble you might experience because of the things I have discovered here."

But I held out, wouldn't sign. I knew enough about the Bureau to realize that if I did sign a statement, eventually I would be fired too. Apparently the rest of the Miami agents felt the same way because none of them would charge Krappman with inadequate supervision, and the ammunition the Director was supplied with at the surprise inspection lacked our signed statements charging malfeasance of the SAC.

I found out later that the information obtained at the surprise inspection would never have to be used because Krappman won at the civil service hearing, or rather Turner lost, and I was doubly happy I had not signed a statement against Krappman.

I sat there in front of the inspector in silence, trying to save myself. But at that very moment the senator already had me slated to be fired.

Then Assistant Director of the F.B.I., William J. Dainard walked into the room, and in twenty seconds restored my Bureau career. "Well, Mr. Ollestad, how are you doing out here in the Miami field office? I remember you from training school well. You were one of the most attentive students I ever had."

He was a stupid old goat. I'd been the only new agent out of the entire class that he hadn't put to sleep. The other guys had dozed at one point or another in his presentations. Because I'd been able to stay awake those few days in class to listen to Bureau war stories, I was saved.

Dainard inquired into the present status of my career. "What squad are you on, Mr. Ollestad? . . . Oh, auto theft, that's a good squad. They get lots of savings and recoveries. They're the bread and butter squad of the F.B.I. Are you learning anything from this inspection? Well, that's good. These inspections don't accomplish their purpose unless we all learn how to become better agents through them."

Dainard turned to a slightly stunned Inspector Lightfoot. "How's my prize pupil doing, Senator?"

I saw the senator's fat fleshy stomach quiver as he folded his tents and silently stole away. "Yes, Mr. Dainard, he's doing fine; Mr. Ollestad will pass this inspection with flying colors."

Some of my fellow FBI agents didn't fare so well in that "surprise inspection."

I'd been lucky—that's why I survived. Dainard remembered me, and that got me through. What had helped a little was the fact that I'd retained enough poise to keep smiling and to answer the Inspector's questions after a little forethought. I didn't have as much to lose by being fired as some of the older agents. My friends might have suspected I was a Communist—or morally undesirable for awhile, but I could have always gone back to a law career and eventually overcome the onus.

But the older agents, guys who were approaching retirement and had homes and families in Miami, really ran scared during the week long inspection. Most of them got so taut and strained pondering all they could lose from a transfer or a dismissal that they couldn't function properly.

Special Agent Richard D. Riley was one of those who had much to lose, and he was overly careful. He reported to the field office at 5:50 every morning of the inspection, did paper work until 8:30 A.M., then charged out of the office, not to be heard from until 6:00 in the evening when he quickly checked in and out of the office. Riley spent the evenings of the "surprise inspection week" glued at home next to his television set, then took sleeping pills at night to help fight off his temporary insomnia.

On the fourth day of the purge, Riley received an early morning telephone call from an Inspector. We agents found out all about it after the inspection was over.

"Hello, is this Special Agent Richard D. Riley?" the voice demanded.

Riley, groggy from the pills he had taken, was uncertain about what his response should be. He sleepily looked at the clock on his bed stand. It was 3:00 A.M. The multitude of special agent's rules whirred through his clouded brain. "Ah . . . well . . . who is this? Just who is this? . . . Sir?"

"Listen Riley," the gruff voice barked, "this is Inspector Green, and the office just received a teletype from Chicago in an interstate transportation of stolen property case, one of yours. You know the rule for that don't you?"

Riley was in a tizzy. . . . The rule against an agent identifying himself to *anybody* over the phone was clear, but on the other hand, the man on the phone said he was an inspector and even though Riley couldn't recognize his voice he sure talked like one. 'They're testing me!' Riley thought. But he said nothing into the phone.

"Mr. Riley, are you going to answer my question?" the voice persisted.

"Look, sir, I don't know who you are, and I'm not going

to discuss any FBI business over the phone. If you have a problem then come into the office tomorrow, the FBI is listed in the first page of your local telephone directory."

"Mr. Riley, do you like your job? Do you like being a special agent of the FBI? . . . Huh?" the voice continued.

"Yes sir," Riley quivered.

"Are you going to come down to the office immediately?

"Yes, sir," Riley mumbled and hung up the phone.

When he arrived at the office the inspectors were waiting. The teletype could have kept until morning, but Riley had been rude over the phone. He should have been ready for the call—the inspectors always picked one night of the inspection week and stayed up phoning agents to see if they were home. But Riley wasn't prepared; and beleaguered by the pills and an irate inspector, he committed several blunders, including a slip of the tongue that the month before he had used a Bureau auto as transportation to dinner. That morning he signed a confession admitting his breach of the rule, and magnified his crime by refusing at the last minute to name the agent who had accompanied him.

The news of Riley's demise spread quickly through the field office, and I, along with the rest of the special agents, was immediately interviewed.

"Have a seat, Mr. Ollestad. Relax."

"Sure, Mr. Dainard," I said.

"I'm not going to waste a lot of Bureau time finding out what I already know, so I'll put it on the line." Dainard then proceeded to do just the opposite. "You know Special Agent Richard D. Riley?"

"Yes sir."

"Were you out with him in a Bureau auto at any time last month?"

"No."

"Have you ever used a Bureau automobile as transportation for personal purposes, such as to go to dinner?"

"No."

"Will you sign this statement to that effect?" Dainard shoved a typewritten statement across the desk. I quickly signed.

Dainard continued after he took up my signed statement. "Well, I suppose you know that Riley used a Bureau auto to go to dinner in last month."

I affected a serious air. "This is the first I've heard of it sir."

"We inspectors just happened to be checking up on him and discovered it. I've had my eye on him for some time. He didn't ring true to me. How about you, Ollestad?"

"He didn't ring true to me either, sir."

The inspection report sending Riley to Butte, Montana, and suspending him without pay for three months was buttressed by his written signed confession of the wrongful use of the Bureau auto, and signed statements by every other agent in the office to the effect that they had never used a Bureau auto to go to dinner.

The whole thing didn't bother me too much; I was getting used to these Bureau maelstroms. And when it was over my dominant feeling was one of gladness—I was pleased that it wasn't I who had incurred the inspector's ire. The Director showed his inherent goodness by not dismissing Riley from the FBI, and as it turned out, the most important aspect of the incident was that the unfortunate agent was not demoted because of the phone insult—the FBI didn't work that way. There was concrete evidence that a Bureau car had been used for dinner. It gave us agents some comfort to know that at any civil service hearing or court proceeding, if Riley would ever object to his suspension, there would be more than ample evidence, legally obtained, to prove the violation. Sixteen inspectors had worked night and day to be sure.

When Riley left for Montana we all had to chip in fifteen dollars to take some of the edge off Riley's loss on the quick sale of his four-bedroom home in Coral Gables. I was glad to do it, it made me feel better. And in the back of my mind I thought that maybe I'd need that kind of help from my fellow agents some day.

I reacted to the Riley affair much better than I had received Fife's request that I change my report on the applicant George Albin. And I was happier about coughing up fifteen dollars for Riley than I had been paying the few cents for the stolen Cokes back in the training school.

As I became more experienced in the Bureau and got farther away from the ivory tower of law school, the adjustments came fairly easy. The difference between the pragmatic cheating on the FBI time sheets every day to keep things running smoothly, and committing perjury in federal court—also to keep things running smoothly—even this difference blended together until it all seemed the same.

# 24

I suspected that it happened often—fudging on your testimony under oath in federal court—but the only incident that I really knew of occurred in another jurisdiction at another time, and I wasn't directly involved.

It began as a routine case. Information had reached the F.B.I. that a federal agent of the United States Treasury Department, Internal Revenue Service, Alcohol and Tobacco Tax Division, was soliciting a bribe from a man suspected of violating the federal firearms statute.

Since the F.B.I. are the police who police the police, the Bureau immediately began investigating the federal officer to determine if he really approached the suspect with an offer to take a $20,000 bribe in return for immunity from prosecution.

The case was initially given to a young charger just out of F.B.I. training school.

"Got a new one for you, Wright," his squad leader informed him. "Some suspect claims that an alcohol and tobacco tax agent approached him for a $20,000 bribe."

He took the file. "What's the agent's name?"

"Jerry Hernstein. Go over to A and TT and see if he's supposed to be investigating the suspect."

"Then what?"

"If it looks like there's something to this accusation, then we'll tail the agent, catch him red-handed."

The new agent went into immediate action in true training school spirit, and reported back that afternoon with the information.

"Hernstein is on the case all right. His suspect is a very wealthy man, but he's queer for illegal firearms. . . . I think we should go all out on this guy Hernstein. Imagine a federal agent soliciting a bribe from a criminal!" The Charger was glad that the Bureau was in charge of keeping the other federal agencies in line. "We'll give the victim $20,000 in marked money—and put that fluorescent dust on the currency so we'll know if Hernstein handled it when we bust him," he suggested.

"Whoa, Charger. Where are we going to get $20,000 cash?" the squad leader wanted to know.

"For Christ's sake, we pay more than that to the wino informants for worthless information." The young agent got a little excited. "Besides, I interviewed the victim today, and he said he'd put up the money himself if the F.B.I. would guarantee that if any of the money was lost, we'd reimburse him. After all, this is a federal violation, and he's helping us."

"Maybe, or he just wants to take the heat off of himself." The squad leader smiled condescendingly. "Now, Charger, just slow down a little here. There's more than one way to skin a cat. The Director is very touchy about any money being lost or unaccounted for."

"It's the risk we have to take, Bernie, it's the only way we can catch this Hernstein red-handed and make an air-tight case against him." He had another thought. "It's also the only way we'll ever know for sure if he is innocent or guilty. If we catch him with the bribery money there will be no innocent explanation. On the other hand, any other kind of activity on his part might, or might not, be legitimate. After all, he is supposed to be investigating this so-called victim—

he might be completely innocent after all—we should be absolutely sure," he protested.

"I can see that I'll have to re-assign this case. You're going to get us all in Bureau type trouble with such recklessness." Bernie could see that the new agent was about to explode with frustration, so he attempted to calm him down. "You can still work the case, you were in on the ground floor and you know the victim. We'll have to call in the other squad leader anyway. In these bribery cases, Hoover takes a personal interest and wants a conviction. It shows that the F.B.I. is doing a good job policing the other federal agencies."

Two days later, Bernie and the other squad leader set up a trap for Hernstein at the victim's office. The new agent helped them set up the microphones.

"We don't need that money plant, charger," Bernie assured him. "We'll also set up a mike in the men's room in case they go in there during the meeting. We don't leave anything to chance."

The three of them then took their places inside the closet of the victim's office when the surveilling agents warned of Hernstein's approach by radio.

As they strained to listen, Hernstein walked into the main office, and without a *word,* both he and the victim walked directly into the men's toilet.

As the three men bounded out of the closet and ran over to the door of the men's room, Bernie whispered reassuringly, "Aren't you glad I thought to put the mike in there?" His smile was effaced by the sound of running water inside the room. Either Hernstein or his victim had turned on a faucet which obliterated their conversations.

The squad leader rushed over to the door of the men's room and put his ear to the door. He was furious at Bernie also.

"God dammit, Bernie, I can't hear a thing that they're saying in there."

After several minutes of unfruitful straining, the squad leader finally broke down the door and arrested Hernstein. The other two assisted. They called in Hernstein's superior at the alcohol and tobacco tax division, then had Hernstein committed to the custody of the United States marshal.

Hernstein was tried for the crime. The entire trial naturally centered around the question of whether Hernstein had come to the office for the bribe money or as a part of his legitimate investigation. Without the marked money or recordings the crux of the government's case was the testimony of the squad leader as to the conversation between Hernstein and the suspect in the men's room, while he was trying to listen with his ear to the door.

The new agent had had some personal doubts about the case, but "after all," the three who had worked the case all agreed, "Hernstein was an objectionable, officious, ugly Jew, and he was probably guilty as hell."

At the first trial the federal judge, sitting as a "thirteenth juror" ordered a new trial after a jury had convicted Hernstein. The judge had doubts about the case. The next trial resulted in a hung jury, they had irreconcilable doubts about the case. A third jury returned a guilty verdict on some of the charges against Hernstein.

The conviction didn't come any too early. Bernie and the squad leader really needed one at that point. The Director had sent out personal letters of commendation after the first jury had convicted, and had taken a personal interest in the case. If they had failed to get a conviction, there would have been letters of censure, or even worse.

The tape recordings placed in the men's room were unintelligible because of the running faucet, so it remained for the squad leader to resolve the reasonable doubts of the jury by his testimony of what was said in the room while he was listening at the door.

His performance was faultless.

"Now, sir, you're in charge of a squad at the local field office of the Bureau, is that true?" the prosecutor asked.

"Yes," our squad leader answered confidently.

Hernstein's superior, a high Treasury Department official, attended the third trial.

The official watched intently as the F.B.I. agent began his testimony. The jury, who had been inattentive with the last witness, leaned forward in their seats with interest. "So this is what a real live F.B.I. agent looks like," was their collective thought.

The squad leader was clean shaven and immaculately dressed, even to the brilliantly shined black shoes. His face was slightly tanned, showing the jury a proper mixture of intellectual and physical fitness. The women appreciated the expensiveness of the navy blue suit he wore. A picture of objectivity, he waited calmly until he was asked a question, then paused before giving a carefully worded, but impressively honest sounding narrative.

"At that time I heard voices coming from across the hall and from a room which I recognized to be a bathroom, a washroom," he said slowly.

"What did you do then?" the assistant United States attorney who was prosecuting the case, prompted.

"I put my ear up to the door and first I heard a voice, which I recognized to be that of the victim, as saying, 'I tried, I tried. I couldn't get it in five days. Sometimes it takes longer.' And then I lifted my head from the door to look at my associates and when I put my ear back to the door I heard the victim continuing: 'It takes seven days.' It appeared to me that I had missed several words during that second or two, whatever it was."

The FBI man was cool. It took a lot of nerve to testify as he did, because he hadn't heard *any* conversation at all.

The jury stirred almost imperceptibly. They felt the witness was going overboard to be fair, as he continued.

" 'It takes seven days. I'll get the money. I told them that I would put up my boat for collateral.' At this point another male voice cut in firmly and said, 'Do you know what a strain this is, going through something like this? You promised you'd have it.' "

The prosecutor interrupted again, "Did there come a time . . . ," but the FBI man wasn't finished with Hernstein yet. He delivered the coup de grace with a sharp nod of his head in the defendant's direction.

"At this point I opened the door and the man in the room with the victim was placed under arrest."

The jury convicted Hernstein, and this time it stuck. Hernstein would have been acquitted without the squad leader's testimony, but no one thought about it too much, because Hernstein was guilty anyway. And besides everyone knew that J. Edgar Hoover fudged a little under oath when he appeared before Congress every year—for the good of the Bureau.

But a few weeks later, Hernstein's defense attorney received a photostat of a letter from Hernstein's boss, the Treasury official who had attended the trial. The attorney immediately notified the United States attorney, who took the letter and turned it over to the F.B.I. for authentication. It passed around the Bureau like a hot poker.

The addressee of the original letter had been purposely blocked out.

The letter read:

U. S. Treasury Department
Internal Revenue Service
Office of Regional Commissioner
          Alcohol and Tobacco Tax Division

Since I last saw you, there have been some very disturbing developments in the Jerry Hernstein trial. An agent of the F.B.I. has testified he overheard a conversation between the victim and Hernstein which concerned money.

I am astounded at such testimony. Immediately after arresting Hernstein, the same agent privately informed me no money had changed hands or was involved. I specifically asked him if there were any witnesses, and he told me Hernstein and the victim had been in a lavatory near the victim's office, and he had put his ear to the door *but could not make out what was being said as the voices were garbled.* He told me if it would have been up to him he never would have arrested Hernstein, but he had no choice as the U. S. attorney's office pushed it. He even phoned me the next day and tried to persuade me to order Hernstein to go to his office to be interrogated. I told him he was imposing on our acquaintanceship, and besides Hernstein was mule-headed and would probably refuse.

It seems to me that my neck is out a mile unless I inform Hernstein's attorney.

Let me know as soon as possible what course of action to take.

Very truly yours,

The writer of the letter died a week after Hernstein was convicted. The photostatic copy of the letter was the only thing the FBI had to work with. It was sent to the FBI lab in Washington, but they came to the conclusion that the signature on the letter was "inconclusive," that they really couldn't tell if the high Treasury official had signed it or not.

It seemed strange at the time that the same F.B.I. Lab that broke the Peter Weinberger kidnapping case in '56 by comparing La Marca's handwriting on the ransom note with millions of samples of handwriting on public documents— driver's licenses, affidavits, and applications, couldn't decide one way or the other by comparing a known signature of this federal official with the signature on the letter. He was a government employee. There must have been hundreds of samples of his signature over at Alcohol and Tobacco Tax. And the government-issued typewriter that was used to type out the letter could be checked in the FBI typewriter library.

The photostat of the letter and the envelope it came in could have been checked for latent fingerprints, to find out what government employees handled it. The squad leader who testified could have been interviewed.

When the new agent made these suggestions, Bernie exploded.

"Jesus, are you crazy? Don't do *anything* unless I tell you. Just sit tight. With the lab's conclusion we can make a reasonable report on this situation and still let it blow over. I just wanted you to sign and OK this lab report."

The Charger didn't catch on right away. "I can question the official's superiors to see if they received the original letter. I'll question the U. S. attorney who tried the case. We'll determine the brand of photostat paper and the weight, bond, size and other physical characteristics that could help find its origin and the people who might have handled the letter. That typewriter should be easy to locate. It'll be a classic F.B.I. case! The triumph of science over crime!" he shouted.

"Listen, Wright, don't push it. Our squad leader already has had a heart attack over this. Literally had an attack. That's why he's been off since last week. Besides, you're in this pretty deep too." Bernie furrowed his brow, trying to threaten the young man.

"I'm not worried, Bernie, I didn't lie in court."

But after that slight skirmish they came to terms. They agreed to cover up the investigation of any possible perjury by one of their fellow F.B.I. agents because it would only have led to their own punishment by the Director, and as they knew so well, Hernstein was guilty anyway so they figured he might as well do his time in prison for attempting the bribe.

Had the incident occurred in the latter stages of my F.B.I. career, I would have reacted in the same way. Since it seems that nothing in the "real world" is ever like it's supposed to be, at this stage in my F.B.I. career I had decided that there were only two ways to go when I was confronted with the necessity of a compromise. I could cry and quit the Bureau, or smile and adjust. I always took the more mature, the smarter route, and adapted my ideas and ideals to fit the mold of the F.B.I. And as I made each adjustment I gained confidence that I could successfully chart a safe course to my twenty-year retirement.

It was relatively easy for me to adapt to the so-called "big problems" that I encountered as an F.B.I. agent. I had learned how to survive inspections (with a little luck) and how to get through "private interviews" by the inspectors unscathed.

Problems of wire tapping, bugging, and "black bag jobs"* or the problems of what the Director was doing in his direction of the F.B.I. back in Washington, these big problems I was able to cope with. When these weighty subjects were discussed by Wally or Laird, they rapidly disintegrated into philosophic dissertations which had little or no direct application to me personally, or to any other of the agents in Miami personally.

All these so-called big problems were really just politics. If you were liberal in your political outlook you were against wire-tapping and so forth; if you were conservative you were for it because you could find imperative reasons for these practices. Most of these big problems didn't bother me because they were necessary to combat crime. I was content to leave the direction and control of the F.B.I. to the Director where it belonged. But I couldn't rationalize the personal problems, the matters of conscience.

The Director may have been correct when he always said, "Take care of the little things, they are important—the big things will take care of themselves," because it was a little thing—a personal problem that kept recurring that I was unable to cope with. It had to do with Jim, the Negro clerk stationed at the Miami office of the F.B.I. He was what you would call a real swinger. He knew music, he knew literature—I didn't know that many guys who had read Dylan

---

*Black bag jobs are illegal searches of homes and apartments conducted by FBI agents to get much needed evidence and intelligence information. The agents gave this procedure its nickname because it is "just like a magician's black bag . . . now you see it, now you don't." There is not much question that the FBI or any other agency charged with intelligence work could not do its required job without recourse to "black bag jobs."

Thomas, but Jim could ramble off his poetry for hours.

Jim didn't dress way out like some of his kinfolk that we would see on the beach from time to time, but a real cool Ivy-League—tight pants, the wing tipped cords, the striped tie, blue button-down shirt, blue blazer—the whole route. A few times we talked in the stock room, I actually forgot that he was colored, but then it would always come up.

"Yeah, Ollestad, you're home free," he'd say. "Big agent of the F.B.I., all those women calling you up night and day, and you get some pretty big bags under your eyes there, boy."

"Oh, yeah," I'd retort automatically, "I understand you're known as the big stud from across the tracks. . . .

"Does it ever bother you that you have to live across the tracks, Jim?"

"Yeah, a little, but not as much as when I was younger. Now I know there's something I can do about it. Old fellows like Leo, and little kids, they got to accept it, but not me. I'm the one who's going to do the work and make it better for 'em."

"Do you really think you can do anything by yourself? It doesn't do any good does it? Just one man?" I asked honestly.

"Hell, yes," Jim answered, "my blood can go down to the Mau Mau Lounge down by the Miami airport at night now and couldn't before. That's because of me right here. The guy you see sitting right here in the stockroom with his feet on the desk. I went there every night for a month until they finally let me in. It finally happened that one of the jazz musicians was blood and he wouldn't play until I sat right up there by the stage and from then on, it has been no sweat."

"Goddamn it, Jim, you've got a lot of nerve. If I were you, I don't think I could do it," I said.

Jim smiled at me, a big wide mischievous grin.

"Well, like I say, Norm, when you're real young, or old, you get mean and all frustrated because you can't do anything about it yourself. But now, I'm almost content. Not quite, but almost, 'cause I know that I'm doing everything I can . . . not too fast . . . not un-cool so I ruin everything; I've got to act as if I expect things the same way a white man expects things . . . I can't get apprehensive and scared and mad, it's got to look like it's free and easy. Like I'm really no different. Pretty soon it'll sink in and the white devils will start thinking like that . . . or their kids will . . . their kids will think that there's never been a difference. Deep down I know I'm never going to accept anything but complete freedom, freedom to fail and to succeed. I'm going to be an FBI agent, but not like Leo. Leo had to beg for it—he really isn't qualified to be an agent. But I will be, and the sons of those blue eyed devils will know in their heart that I'm qualified, there won't be any question. Leo does more harm than good for our blood because every time whites see him, it reinforces their old ideas of the black man's inferiority—when they see that he doesn't deserve it. It would be better for us if Leo were still a janitor or a clerk. The sham hurts us, Norm."

"Jim, you're going to have more trouble convincing some of these rebels than you think. It'll be like trying to convince them that the Bible doesn't preach segregation—or that Jesus was a black man." I was probably in bad taste, but Jim didn't look bothered. He went on, enthusiastic about his grand design.

"The big difference is that Jesus wasn't a black man—he was white—no matter what any one argues," Jim said. "And when I knock at the front door of an Atlanta, Georgia, household in a year or two as an FBI agent, there'll be no quibbling about it. I'll be on the front porch in my charcoal grey suit, charcoal hat, *and* charcoal *face,* and I'll talk and act like I'm an FBI agent and I will have earned it and I'll be qualified."

Jim got up slowly from the desk and came over to me. "And the Southern Belle who answers the door may not accept it—but what about her little boy and girl watching television in the front room? They'll see me—probably the only FBI agent they'll *ever* see—and no matter what is preached or argued to them after that—they'll have *seen* a black agent and they'll accept it. That's why I'm going to hang in here until I become an agent, and I'm expecting to go to the F.B.I. Academy like any other new agent. Just like I belonged there, and it'll get easier and easier until finally no one will think twice about it. It's really very simple when you analyze it. My path is clear, Norm. I'm not as flashy as Jackie Robinson or Dick Gregory, but I'm doing as much good in my own way, I think, and pretty soon people, even down South here will accept a Negro F.B.I. agent the same way they accept a Negro entertainer or athlete."

I got so carried away with Jim's plan, I forgot I was white for a moment. "What can I do Jim?" I asked enthusiastically.

"Man, you're white, I'm black. You can't go out and *do* anything. Because you're not blood Norm, I'll never be able to explain it to you, but you just can't go out and *do* a thing. Everytime you go down to the colored section as a social worker or with a Christmas package, you're rehearsing our inferiority . . . you're making it worse."

I looked a little dumbfounded, and then Jim explained it and I understood.

"Norm, there will come a day when the opportunity to treat us as equals, to treat a Negro as a human being, will come to you; it'll look you right in the face. Not only won't you not have to go out looking for it, you won't be able to avoid it. Your chance to do us good or evil will come—it always does—where you don't want it to come . . . and then you'll have your chance."

I'd already had a chance like that, back at the Delta Sigma Phi Fraternity House at U.C.L.A. and I'd muffed it. A Negro by the name of Rafer Johnson, a big lanky fellow, had rushed for the white fraternities. I guess he, like Jim, wasn't convinced of any inferiority, and he acted just like he had a right to be chosen. Not obnoxious, not pushy, but just that quiet confidence that a star football player has when he goes through fraternity rushing . . . like he knew there was a spot for him.

The chance had come early one morning about three A.M. in the chapter room of the frat house while we groggily voted on each applicant as we methodically choked on gin and black cigars, as was the custom. The fraternity president droned out Rafer's name and almost everyone woke up. There was a moment of silence, and then the president started to call for a vote, since it looked like he'd be summarily rejected and there was no use wasting time in discussion. It only took three black balls to "ding," or reject a *rushee* and keep him out of the fraternity and it was pretty obvious that there were more than three in-brothers of Delta Sigma Phi that didn't want "a nigger" in the house.

But before the president could speak, one of the brothers, Frank Randa, I think it was, or Jay Strong, one of them spoke up. "I know you guys will ding Rafer, but I think we should discuss him. He's one of the sharpest guys I've ever met, and I think he's going to rush this house."

The president took charge quickly. "Of course he's sharp

—I'd like to take him myself, this house needs some more athletes in it, but it'll never go with the sororities. What will the Phi Phis think? Or the Thetas? No discussion, we'll have a vote now, in case he comes around here."

The president still was not in complete control. There was still time to act, to at least throw the meeting open to discussion. I could have done it if I had spoken out right at that moment. At that time I was an upper classman. I played the guitar at the fraternity beach parties. I fixed up the freshmen with sorority girls when they couldn't get a date on Saturday night. I was a "zany," a college funny man, and as such, strangely enough, wielded more influence than the president of the house.

But I let the moment pass, I did the wrong thing. It was against my conscience, it was contrary to what I wanted to do, but I hesitated because of the social pressure. I didn't want to be defeated, to lose my prestige, my standing within the house. So I sat silently, while three zit-faced brothers, guys who weren't qualified to carry Rafer Johnson's sweaty jock strap, blackballed him from the Delta Sigma Phi. Rafer joined another Caucasian fraternity, became student-body president of U.C.L.A., and won a gold medal in the Olympics for the United States in the decathlon event. So it didn't matter much to him, but it bothered me for a long time.

Jim was right, those chances would come. And they were more difficult than carrying a sign and walking in a freedom march, because the acts Jim was talking about couldn't be rehearsed, they couldn't be scheduled, you had to act from instinct, from the heart and emotion, not from the mind— the planning brain. So if you were afraid to speak out or afraid to act it showed.

I looked intently into Jim's laughing brown eyes. I saw friendship.

The last time I saw Jim, I looked into his face again and found intense hatred. He'll hate me for the rest of his life.

That little, inevitable thing that happened to change him was the annual F.B.I. office party. As Opal Long had feared, Jim showed up at Biscayne Park at two in the afternoon that Sunday. He even brought a date, a good looking young Negro lady, so now there two Negroes at the F.B.I. office party, not just one.

That Jim had a lot of guts. The two Negroes walked right up in the middle of our soft ball game; they didn't ask to play, didn't even seem to want to. They just sat down on the sidelines and watched the game like nothing was wrong, just like they were white or something. It was the third inning, and my side, auto theft, was behind to the security squad 6 to 5. But I was on second base with the tying run and only one out.

Then all of a sudden I was standing alone at second base. Everyone else had left the field. The game was over.

Jim was looking at me standing out there on second base to see if I would leave the field too. To see if I was one of those "blue eyed devils" he talked about occasionally. I didn't want to leave the diamond. I wanted to stay right there on the field until everyone in the office came back and finished the game. I even wanted Jim and his girl friend to play on our side. It seemed such a pity to ruin a good game of baseball.

Everyone at the picnic had been having such a wonderful time and I was filled with a feeling of deep pride to be a fellow F.B.I. agent playing baseball with the rest of the fellows, helping them out on raids and possibly saving another agent's life someday. The association made me proud for the most part—they were an outstanding group of men; on the other hand, Jim had become a personal friend of mine too.

For a split second as I stood out on second base at Biscayne Park, I allowed my desire to be liked by a group of fine, high-calibre men to overcome a deep-seated conviction of what was right, or wrong; and when Fife saw me standing out there and waved me off, I left second base, walked right past Jim and his girl and joined the rest of the F.B.I. office personnel who were grouped around one of the picnic tables.

I've always wondered what the Cracker would have done if he'd been there. I can't believe he would have done the same as Fife.

At first Fife tried the friendly approach. I could hear him talking to Jim and his girl.

"Well, how are you today, Jim?" Fife didn't realize it but he then insulted Jim by assuming he didn't know enough to introduce his girl friend, and before Jim could speak he continued on. "Howdy ma'm. My name is T. A. Fife, and I'm Jim's boss down at the F.B.I."

The supervisor was a little taken aback to see that Jim's pretty friend *wasn't* taken aback. She introduced herself firmly, and loudly enough so the rest of us could hear. "Good afternoon, Mr. Fife, I'm Sondra Bates. Jim has told me all about you." She smiled, so Fife knew it was all good talk about him.

For a minute I thought it was going to turn out all right. Everyone seemed real friendly. But then Fife got to the point.

"Miss Bates, you know that Jim is going to be a special agent of the F.B.I. some day if he plays his cards right. He's got all the qualifications right now. A college degree, he's intelligent, and a physical specimen. The only thing he lacks right at the moment is judgment." He stared at Jim, hoping to intimidate him, but Jim looked square back into the supervisor's eyes and didn't smile.

Fife then tried a new tactic. He whispered to the two Negroes. I was close enough to hear him.

"Look Jim, why don't you leave now and we'll discuss this Monday morning. I'm sympathetic, I'm on your side, but some of the people back there—a minority of them, very few of them—they're putting me on the spot. Let's discuss it Monday morning. Now why don't you both go right now, and I'll make it up to you, believe me. I'll recommend that you be made an agent—even before your three years as a clerk are over. That's a big raise in pay Jim—I'll make it up to you Jim. Talk to him Sondra, that's a lot of money, special agent's pay. Talk to him."

The Negro girl started to turn toward Jim, but he waved her away with a short flick of his hand. Fife was on the spot. He was frustrated. He lost his temper.

"Listen you God damned nigger son of a bitch," he yelled. "If you don't get right out of here, I'm going to throw you out."

Sondra turned away with her hands on her face and ran across the ball field. Jim didn't move.

Fife tried to assume a threatening pose, but he was too fat to be formidable. And it was obvious that he alone wasn't going to move Jim an inch. He made several threatening gestures like he was going to hit Jim, but the Negro didn't even flinch. I think that Jim was hoping Fife would strike him so he could knock the supervisor's block off.

Then Eaton Alderton decided he'd make a few points with his supervisor. He motioned for the rest of the agents to follow him and when they all got up to Fife, he stepped up in front of Fife and announced. "You can't talk to an agent of the F.B.I. like that! Now get on out of here, before there's bloodshed." Alderton was so stupid that he didn't realize that Jim hadn't said a word since he arrived at the park. Alderton did make his points with Fife that day though, because when Jim saw it was no use, he walked away.

Jim came to work Monday morning like nothing was wrong and no one in the office let on like anything had happened. But I hated Fife with a passion from that day forward. Or maybe it was myself I hated.

And as luck would have it, I had to go out with S. A. Eaton Alderton on an assignment that very same Monday after the incident. I suppose he thought he was a big hero in my eyes for protecting Fife and saving the office party. As we drove over the Miami Beach causeway, he re-created the whole sordid picture, as if I hadn't been right there—as if I'd missed something.

"I don't know quite why I did it Norm, but somebody had to take the bull by the horns. I usually don't take chances."

"Big chance. He had forty agents right with him," I thought. I'd like to have seen him take Jim on alone.

Eaton continued. "I just can't afford to take any chances in this man's F.B.I., Norm, I've got my wife and kids to think about. A lot of agents goof off all the time and everyone thinks they are regular guys, but that's a very *childish* attitude, because if they get fired, what are they giving up? A good pension—$8,900 a year for the rest of their life, a complete medical program for their whole family, and the pride and prestige that goes with being a special agent, and an associate of the Director."

"There are exceptional men in this Bureau," I answered lamely, just to make conversation. "The Cracker, Wally Post —exceptional men."

Alderton laughed, and partially turned his head toward me, keeping his eyes on the road ahead. "Be serious Norm, those guys aren't going anywhere in this Bureau. To advance in the F.B.I., you've got to practice self-discipline, like the Director, adhere to the rules and stop all this fudging that goes on all the time. How can Wally and Spence expect to enforce the law when they are breaking the agents' rules all the time? To enforce discipline you have to have it yourself."

We were stopped at a traffic light and Alderton turned and looked at me. He suddenly became friendly and sincere.

"I'm going to let you in on a little secret because I like you Norm, and I hope that you'll shape up a little so you can advance in the FBI. I've memorized a passage from a speech by J. Edgar Hoover which I've lived by since I came into the FBI. Let's see if I can remember it . . . do you want to hear it Norm?"

"Uh . . . oh . . . yeah, sure, Eaton," I lied. As the signal light turned green and we started up, Alderton, the supervisor's spy, began reciting the Director's speech.

"In my business I meet a good many undesirable characters. Murderers, robbers, arsonists, rapists, kidnappers —they pass in an unending procession before the eyes of the Federal Bureau of Investigation. Some of these hoodlums are old; some—far too many—are young. Some are rich—some are poor. Some are deceptively handsome, some repulsively ugly. Frequently I am asked if, in this strange foregathering of the nation's filthiest criminals, I find any common denominator, and I am able to answer without hesitation, *Yes, they are all liars.*

"Possibly it is because of my special opportunities for observing what happens to human beings when the old fashioned virtues are forgotten or wantonly discarded— perhaps it is because I am just old fashioned myself— but I look back with fond eyes to the day when a boy or girl sat at his school desk writing upon a copybook the old maxim that Honesty is the best policy. As dripping water wears away a stone, so did that old maxim, written and rewritten, pound itself into the subconscious brain, until a boy or girl said naturally to himself, 'Honesty is the best policy.' It was his bulwark when some tempter came beside him; it was a strong right arm about his shoulders when someone suggested the commission of a theft. Instinctively, that old copybook maxim would arise in time of need. There would be the stirrings of warning from the subconscious: Don't do this. Don't make an idiot of yourself. Honesty is the best policy.

"Crime prevention is as simple as that."

Alderton let out a big dramatic sigh. "Almost poetry, isn't it, Norm? The Director's own words."

I was tempted to tell Alderton that I'd seen him cheat on the number one register that very morning, but decided against it. I couldn't even bring myself to talk to the guy after that speech, so we sat all afternoon in the car and recorded auto license numbers in front of a "top hoodlum's" home without a word spoken between us.

# 25

Thereafter, in a flurry of activity I attempted to hold on to my agent's job. But although I fought it constantly, my premonition—that another crisis would arise with Jim and that I would be found wanting again—grew stronger inside of me.

Following the disaster at the office picnic I worked my own cases with an almost religious fervor. The Cracker had told me to "run with patience" as I investigated a Federal violation. I suppose he meant that I should do everything possible to solve the crime and locate the criminal and then be patient and let things work out. But I wasn't crafty enough for that, so I "ran doggedly," and let my stubbornness crack the case for me.

Like the master check writer I was looking for. Lessing Tolov was his name, and he'd written so many bogus checks on out-of-state banks that he'd been classified by the FBI laboratory as a "master check writer." He'd never been apprehended. He used a number of good ruses and impersonations to get the checks cashed and he had no fatal weaknesses —didn't drink or gamble or run around with women. Or so it seemed, he didn't have any weaknesses.

I jokingly showed Murph the Surf the photograph of Tolov one day and commented that "that's what a *real* check passer looks like."

"Hell, I know that guy," Murph said.

"Are you kidding?" I asked. "I'm looking for him right now. How do you know him?"

"Well, I don't exactly know him, but I think I've seen him before," Murph admitted.

"You're the same old bull slinger, Murph, even to your friends," I said. "You'll never change."

"No . . . I mean I've seen him around the Thunderbird Hotel. . . . I know what it is . . . sure. Listen. He's married to the comedian at the Thunderbird . . . to the guy who M.C.'s the show at the Thunderbird."

"Married to the *guy?*" I asked.

"Yeah, you know, they're both queer."

"So," I thought to myself, "Lessing Tolov did have an Achilles heel after all."

I knew that my fantastic stroke of luck couldn't last, so I resolved to apprehend my fugitive check writer immediately. I waited around the hotel all day, called into the FBI office every three hours, and in the evening I staked out at the hotel night club. The MC did three shows, but his "wife," Lessing Tolov, never made an appearance.

At 3:00 A.M. I tailed the MC as he left the night club, but he only went upstairs to his room at the Thunderbird and went to bed. Tolov was not there.

The next day I followed the same routine but caught no sign of my check passer. Apparently the master check writer was "cheating" on his mate because he was spending his nights—and days, away from the home nest. It bothered the MC as much as it did me. I couldn't get another agent to spell me in my surveillance, so I gutted it out alone.

About the fourth day I began to feel that my fellow FBI agents were correct in their appraisal that I was wasting my time staking out a wild lead with such unsubstantiated information. But I needed a triumph, a success to keep me going in the F.B.I., so I stuck it out. When it was apparent that the MC of the Thunderbird show was going crazy over his lost lover, I had Murphy approach him with some information that he'd seen his "wife" down by the Americana Hotel the night before. "That's funny," the MC huffed, "he usually stays at the Edgewater when he gets these silly wild hares."

I hot-footed it over to the Edgewater and began my investigation afresh. The manager identified Tolov by my photograph and promised he'd call me when Tolov came in. Exhausted as I was after a fruitless four-day surveillance, I took him at his word and went back to the FBI office, then home.

The Manager crossed me. He didn't call.

When I arrived at the Edgewater Hotel the next morning, the day man told me that the man whose picture I showed him had indeed spent the night and had left at 8:00 in the morning. But Tolov hadn't checked out. I parked in that hotel lobby until 2:00 A.M. when Tolov and a friend walked through the lobby and went upstairs to their room. I called the F.B.I. office, and this time I talked Wally into coming down and helping me with the apprehension.

Within an hour we'd busted down the door to Tolov's room, caught him in bed with his new boy friend, got him to "cop out" on about a hundred bad checks he'd passed, and had him safely tucked away in the Dade County Jail.

It made me feel especially good to bust the door down and put a stop to some of the crime and moral decay that seemed to be so prevalent on the Beach. I think it was a way of fighting off my own guilty feelings.

And I used stubbornness to catch the trail of another intrepid check passer, the "hot walker." He was an exercise boy and "hot walker" for thoroughbred race horses. He'd been coming into Miami during the race season every year and before he left he'd inevitably pass a large amount of bad checks. He was crafty though, he knew that the F.B.I. would never prosecute a bad check, even an interstate bad check if he used his true name on the worthless draft. The Bureau simply doesn't prosecute on "true name" checks. But toward the end of the racing season this year he'd slipped up. He'd written a bad check for one-hundred-twenty dollars and endorsed it, then used it to pay for some furniture at a department store.

I was assigned the case, but I just missed him. He had left for Monmouth Race Track in New Jersey two days before I came to his house and talked to one of his children.

But I was confident that I had him. All I had to do was obtain some samples of his handwriting from his wife (who was still in Miami with their six children), send the handwriting samples to the F.B.I. lab and have them compare the writing with the handwriting of the maker of the bogus check. Then when I got an identification, I could present the case to the assistant United States attorney in Miami, get a complaint, a fugitive warrant, then teletype the Newark, New Jersey, field office to go out and pick up my fugitive. Since my bad check man wasn't in Miami he'd be classified as a "fugitive," even though we all knew exactly where he was. I'd get a statistic for a case opened, solved, and a conviction, and another fellow agent in Newark would get a statistic for capturing a "fugitive"—maybe even a letter of commendation from the Director.

But his wife avoided me like she knew what was going to happen to her husband. She worked in a market to help keep all her kids in food and clothes, as I found out when I tried to contact her during the day. But she wouldn't come after work either.

After two days of the run around I started to get mad. The kids would talk to me freely and I resolved to find out where she worked, then confront her on the job. But I had second thoughts. In the first place, I figured out, she's not likely to have any hand-writing samples of her husband at work, but if I interview her at home I can pick them up at the time I get a good incriminating statement. But the second, and real reason was that after seeing her situation I was a little soft toward her. I made the mistake of getting personally touched by her hopeless situation. Six kids, husband away—husband practically a fugitive. So I figured that the least I could do would be to work it so she didn't get fired.

After two nights of staking out her home, I wore her down.

I caught her coming home at 4:00 A.M. I advised her of her constitutional rights—that she didn't really have to talk to me, etc., but I acted like she was supposed to talk to me—like I assumed she was going to. I followed her into the house and sat down. She was so taken aback that she talked. After she gave me a full confession which implicated her husband, she begged me for a second chance.

"There's nothing I can do about it, Mrs. Williams," I answered. "The prosecution of this case is up to the United States attorney's office. The F.B.I. never takes a side one way or the other—we don't express our opinions whether or not to prosecute. We just report the facts as they are and leave it to the government attorneys to prosecute or not." I talked coolly and efficiently.

"Will it help if I make restitution—if I pay the money back —make the check good?" she pleaded.

"Look, Mrs. Williams, I just told you that that will be up to the government attorney, I don't have anything to say about it. Besides, why didn't you think about this when your husband passed all those bad checks you just told me about?" I scolded.

"Mr. Ollestad, it's almost 7:00 o'clock in the morning. The store will open at 9:00. Will you please wait until I pay for the check before you turn your report in, then you can at least put it in the report that the money's been paid?"

"...Yeah, OK. I'll do that much for you. I'll go have some breakfast and check into the office, and I'll be back here at 9:00. You'd better be here," I warned her.

When I returned she was waiting out in front of her house looking like a wild animal who had just been cornered. I drove her over to the store and marched her into the cashier's office. She pulled out her money—one hundred and twenty dollars worth of crumpled up fives and tens.

"Oh, so you've come to pay up and live like an honest woman," the smart aleck cashier cracked. The woman cashier used her authority to its fullest. She treated both of us like peasants, and irritated me. I looked at the contract Mr. and Mrs. Williams had signed to buy the furniture. It was usurious. With all the high interest and outrageous "service charges," they were paying the store one-hundred twenty dollars for about seventy-five dollars worth of furniture. And it happened that even one-hundred twenty dollars wasn't enough.

"That'll be one-hundred fifty dollars with the late payment and collection charge," the pompous cashier announced.

"I've only got one-hundred twenty dollars—it's my whole pay for three weeks' work," Mrs. Williams almost cried.

"Sorry, you're not getting this release until I get one-hundred fifty dollars." The cashier held the note up to Mrs. Williams as bait.

"Can't you let me pay you the other thirty dollars in three weeks when I get my next pay check?" Mrs. Williams begged. "My husband's going to go to jail, then what'll I do? He helps out with the kids, I can't earn enough to feed them by myself." Mrs. Williams prostrated herself in front of the cashier's window.

The cashier obviously enjoyed this immensely, but wouldn't budge from the hundred fifty dollars. "Why didn't you think about this when you wrote this illegal check?" she asked contemptuously. I gulped when I realized that I'd just posed the same question to Mrs. Williams earlier that morning. I hoped that didn't put me in the same class as that woman cashier.

Then in a maudlin, impetuous move, I jerked out three ten dollar bills from my wallet, threw them down on the cashier's counter and left the store immediately. "Mrs. Williams will have to get her own ride to work," I thought.

I presented the Williams bad check case to the United States attorney later that morning.

"Yes, sir, Mr. Ollestad, what is it?" The AUSA asked as I entered his office.

"Got a case to present to you for your prosecutive opinion," I answered.

"Good, what have you got?"

After I outlined the evidence and told him that I hadn't had time to get an FBI lab check on the handwriting but I had the subject's wife's statement which incriminated him, he then began questioning me.

"Well, Ollestad, looks like we've got enough to successfully prosecute this guy for interstate transportation of stolen property—checks—but how does the FBI feel about it? Is it going to be a waste of the taxpayers' money to convict this guy? What are the circumstances surrounding the check? Do you want to go on him or not?"

"Mr. Barker, you know it's not up to me—whether to prosecute or not. The FBI just investigates, we just get facts and leave it up. . . ."

"Don't give me that bull shit, Ollestad, there hasn't been an FBI agent that *ever* presented a case to me that didn't tell me which way he wanted me to go on it. . . . You know, stuff like 'The Director's very interested in a prosecution in this case' . . . or 'We'll never find this guy—why don't you dismiss this case in the interest of justice?" You know . . . So what way do you want me to go in this case Ollestad?"

"Well, restitution of the check has been made in this case," I offered.

"OK, case dismissed in the interests of justice," the attorney said.

And so I tried to keep going in the FBI, playing God, taking sides in my cases—dealing out punishment and rewards to the unfortunates I hunted—kind of the same way J. Edgar Hoover did to us agents. And it was a comfortable role to play; it was pleasant to be a special agent of the FBI when you could do that. There were a lot of thrilling experiences for me as a young agent.

I was in Miami on the day when the Bay of Pigs invasion of Cuba failed, and through Wally I had known in advance what the outcome would be. All of us agents had also known in advance the day that the invasion was to occur. It made me feel like an insider and a person in the "know" as far as espionage and world events were concerned.

And when someone would hijack a commercial airplane to Havana, Cuba, we F.B.I. agents in Miami would be put on twenty-four hour alert. After the United States Government negotiated the return of the aircraft they would invariably land in Miami and I, along with the rest of the agents, would be called upon to search these aircraft and interview the passengers in order to identify the hijacker. It was always a heady experience for me, a man in my 20's, to press my way through the crowds at the airport and the photographers, and the television cameras, and make my way into the airplane where no ordinary men were allowed—where even the press was barred, where only F.B.I. agents like me could go.

If I had only been able to forget Jim, I could have made my twenty-year span with ease. But every time I walked past the stockroom, or found it necessary to go into Jim's room for supplies, I was reminded of my own personal failure at the office picnic in Biscayne Park.

Jim never talked to me much after that day in the park. It wasn't as though he was hostile or mad, there just wasn't anything to talk about after what had happened. I tried it a couple of times—tried to laugh and joke with Jim, and once I was even able to make him smile, but even on that occasion his lips were smiling, but the rest of his face was not.

Then one bright, calm, hot Sunday afternoon as I lay on the sand between the Thunderbird Hotel and the ocean with Murph the Surf and some of his beach boy buddies, I had the distinct unmistakable feeling that I wasn't going to make it for twenty years in the FBI. In fact from that moment on, I couldn't stand it that I was an agent and Jim the Negro was not—and I couldn't stomach another day of secretly fighting him and his purpose by "smiling and adjusting" to the hypocritical existence of an FBI agent. And I knew that

I would be called upon sooner or later to "treat Jim as a human being" and I'd fail again. It would come when I didn't expect it, like at the picnic, and I'd do the wrong thing again. I thought of quitting the FBI.

I quickly shook off the idea and sat up and started to listen to Murphy and his buddies' small talk on the beach, hoping that would cheer me up, but my attitude persisted. Murphy sort of impressed me at that moment as the Miami Beach equivalent of Malibu's king of the surf-bums, they both waved their hands in the same way when they talked.

"Look at all those surfers out there and not a wave in sight," Murphy said as he gestured toward fifteen young fellows sitting on surf boards on the completely calm ocean. "You know, I'm thinking of giving up surfing," Murphy continued. "If you can get fifteen kooks out in the water when the wave of the day is nine inches high, something is wrong. I remember the time, Ollestad, when we had that perfect swell at Daytona Beach—perfect Malibu type tubes and they were really holding up. All the local kooks up at Daytona, with their redwood nineteen foot 'Queen Mary' boards, said that the surf wasn't big enough, but it was the best shaped four feet I've ever seen in Florida. We were the only two guys out. Don't get days like that any more around here and when we do, there are just too many people, too crowded."

As Murphy stood there spouting in retrospect about the good old pioneer days of Florida surfing, I realized that I was right back where I started. I still knew that there was something better for me, but it wasn't to be had just by joining the F.B.I., or any other agency.

Until that day on the beach at the Thunderbird Hotel, I had always thought that I could join some organization, or associate with some group of men and that that would make me happy, and successful, but I now realized that I would have to find that "something better," within myself—that the outside world in which I lived would never be happy until I conformed to the code of conduct that had been ingrained in me when I was a child.

Something as corny as the Golden Rule had caused my defeat. I could no longer be a part of the F.B.I. when I knew that I was not doing unto Jim and Leo as I would want them to do unto me.

And so, abruptly, I said "Goodbye" to Murph and his entourage of no-good surfer-bums, and prepared to return to an association with their counterparts in Malibu, California.

"Well, the hell with it," I said, "I've had it. For three-hundred and sixty days out of the year the surf in Florida is zero. To hell with you guys, I'm going back to California." I picked up my surf board which had been lying propped up against the sea wall in front of the hotel, and tied it to the top of my black Volkswagen. Murphy came over to say "Goodbye."

"You really going home, Ollestad?"

"Yeah, Murphy."

"OK, adios, Agent Zero," Murph said. "Maybe I'll see you in California."

"Sure, Murph the Surf," I answered, "maybe I'll see you at Malibu."

"Or maybe you'll read about me in the papers one of these days—'Murph the Surf rides giant forty foot wave from Faggot Head to the Collins Street pier.'"

"Yeah, Murph the Surf, maybe I'll read about you in the papers some day," I told him.

Supervisor Fife was philosophical when I told him. "Well, certainly, Mr. Ollestad, I'm not going to talk you out of it, but you'll realize your mistake before you're gone two months. I'll type up a good letter of resignation, thanking the Director for his guidance and training and we'll send it out right away."

Two weeks later I walked out of the F.B.I. office in Miami for the last time. I knew I wouldn't miss the fat-assed Bobbsey twins, Fife and Alderton, at all, but Wally felt bad about it, even said so.

As I drove my car through the bottle-neck of traffic collected at the entrance to the Sunshine State Parkway and prepared to drive north to Highway 80 and then west to California, I came close to crying. I had seen the old Georgia Cracker wave goodbye to me from across the main office as I went out the door. I was almost positive his lips said, "Goodbye and good luck." I hadn't heard it of course, I was too far away, but I was sure. "Hell, Spence didn't have to do that," I thought, "I'm not an inspector. Guess he really wanted me to have good luck."

And as I look back, I feel it was too bad I couldn't make it work like Sam back in Washington, D.C., or like Wally, or the Cracker. And eventually, there would be a Bureau without the Master.